The Giant Book of
IQ Puzzles

The Giant Book of IQ Puzzles

David J. Bodycombe

Magpie Books, London

Constable & Robinson Ltd
3 The Lanchesters
162 Fulham Palace Road
London W6 9ER
www.constablerobinson.com

First published in the UK by Robinson,
an imprint of Constable & Robinson Ltd 1997

This edition published by Magpie Books,
an imprint of Constable & Robinson Ltd 2005

A copy of the British Library Cataloguing in
Publication Data is available from the British Library

ISBN 1-84529-198-0

Printed and bound in the EU

1 3 5 7 9 10 8 6 4 2

CONTENTS

(Answers are at the end of
each round of ten puzzles)

v

ABOUT THE AUTHOR

David J. Bodycombe was born in Darlington, England in 1973. Over seven years his creations have appeared in a national puzzle magazine, the *Daily Telegraph*, *Mensa Magazine* and on television.

For five years, he was one of the games creators for the UK Channel Four programme *The Crystal Maze*.

After graduating in Mathematics from the University of Durham in 1995, David moved to Kingston-upon-Thames, Surrey, where he currently works for a management consultancy company.

By the same author

The Mammoth Book of Brainstorming Puzzles

Edited by the author

Giant Family Puzzles

Giant Crazy Puzzles

INTRODUCTION

Carnival owners certainly are on to a good thing. The crowds roll up to hand over their money and then they go away happy. So why do we play their games at all? Because they're fun, and I hope that's what you'll have when playing the 330 puzzles in this book.

For those of you who have already crossed paths with my first book, *The Mammoth Book of Brainstorming Puzzles*, you will know that I aim to give my puzzles a different "spin", whether devising completely new concepts or giving classic teasers an unexpected sting in the tail. Some of the puzzles are straightforward, others are slightly sneaky, and the challenge is to work out which are which. And that's before you even start to solve the puzzle itself!

Once again I have provided a scoring system for the more competitive reader. If, however, you want to drop in to a particular stall that takes your fancy, feel free to do so. I have included clues to the puzzles – see page ix for further details.

So roll up for all the fun of the fair. And once you've paid for this book you don't even need to pay me an admission charge.

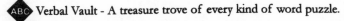

Every day the Carnival has ten games for you to attempt. Although there are many locations within the Carnival, some of which you will meet on your travels, you will find that the following five stalls contain the puzzles themselves:

 Verbal Vault - A treasure trove of every kind of word puzzle.

 Number Cruncher - The fun house for figures.

 Picture Palace - Can you defeat our visual vexations?

Logic Lounge - Take a seat, put your feet up and listen to these logic problems and lateral thinking riddles.

Mystery Box - Anything and everything else!

The number of points you can win for each puzzle varies from two to ten points. If you are completely stuck on a puzzle, don't give up as help is at hand. Turn to pages 477–497 where you will find a clue for the puzzle you are stuck on. However, **if you read the clue you only get half the points available for that puzzle.**

Wrong answers score 0 points.

A number of puzzles have a bonus question. If you think you've solved the main puzzle, correct answers to bonus puzzles earn you an extra 5 points. However, you can only claim these points if you got the main puzzle correct.

Keep a track of your scores as you go around the Carnival. Every so often there is a "Test Your Strength" machine so that you can determine if you're a logic lightweight or a brainy brute!

Happy puzzling.

ROUND 1

Use this page to keep track of your score. Carry your total forward to the next round of puzzles.

Answers to Round 1 puzzles are on pages 12–14.

Category		Points	Your Score
ABC	1. BUILDING BLOCKS	10	◇
	2. TELEPHONY	2	◇
123	3. TREE WEAVE	8	◇
✓✗	4. IF TRUTH BE TOLD...	10	◇
123	5. SNOOKERED	6	◇
	6. IN PERSPECTIVE	2	◇
✓✗	7. CHECK IT, MATE	8	◇
123	8. EVEN-ING ALL	4	◇
ABC	9. ROUNDABOUTS	4	◇
	10. PUMP UP THE VOLUME	6	◇

TOTAL FOR THIS ROUND ◇

\+ Bonuses (5 points each) ◇

\+ Running total from previous round ⟨0⟩

TOTAL SO FAR ◈
(carry forward to next round)

The diagram below shows a pile of 36 toy bricks, each one bearing a letter. By taking the bricks one at a time, you can spell out 6 words, clues to which are provided.

You must only take bricks that are not supporting other bricks – so you'll have to take the "A" as your first letter and then you must decide whether the "T" or "N" should come next. When you have finished, the three starred blocks will remain.

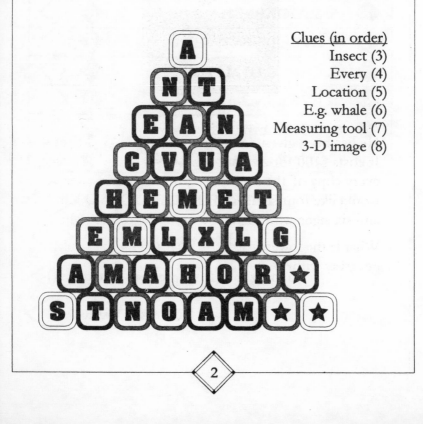

Clues (in order)
Insect (3)
Every (4)
Location (5)
E.g. whale (6)
Measuring tool (7)
3-D image (8)

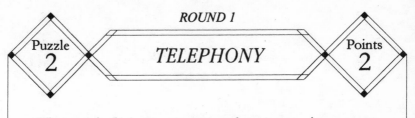

The carnival owner wants to place some signs around the grounds so that visitors can see where the nearest public telephone is situated. He wants it to look something like this:

He has been given a quotation from his local firm. It costs $100 for a sign to be designed, and $10 for every copy of the sign that's printed. The owner would like four signs with the arrow pointing left, and six signs with the arrow pointing to the right.

What is the lowest total cost that the owner could get away with?

Children visiting the carnival are often challenged to run the Tree Weave Race. The participant starts at point A, and then runs to points B, C, D then back to A. For each leg of the trip the children always choose one of the several shortest routes available through the trees.

There are 625 routes available to the children for the whole trip. How many routes would there be if they ran from 1, to 2, to 3, to 4, then back to 1?

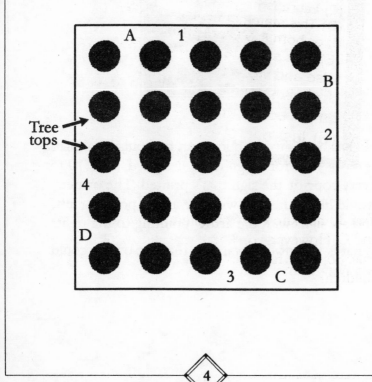

Tree
tops

IF TRUTH BE TOLD...

The stall holder of the Logic Lounge, Lateral Larry, poses you a question.

"Let me tell you about my children, Jack, Keith and Laura. If you want to win this game, you have to work out what you can deduce from the following statements." He hands you a card:

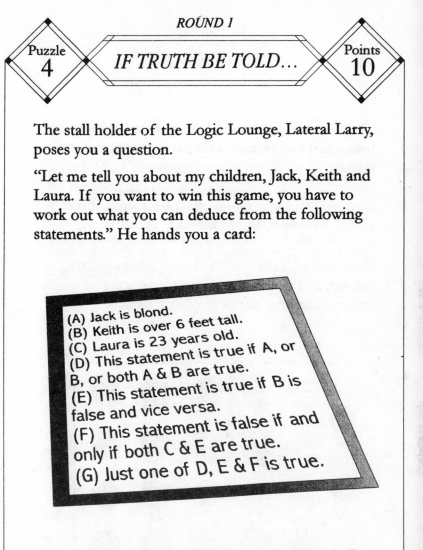

(A) Jack is blond.
(B) Keith is over 6 feet tall.
(C) Laura is 23 years old.
(D) This statement is true if A, or B, or both A & B are true.
(E) This statement is true if B is false and vice versa.
(F) This statement is false if and only if both C & E are true.
(G) Just one of D, E & F is true.

You do not know anything about statements A, B and C. However, you know that statement G is true. So, what facts can you deduce about Larry's children?

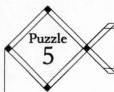
The English game of snooker uses eight different balls, each one scoring a different number of points:

Red = 1 point; Yellow = 2 points
Green = 3 points; Brown = 4 points
Blue = 5 points; Pink = 6 points
Black = 7 points; White = counts as -4

Place one of each into the box so that each row, column and diagonal adds up to the amount shown. The blue has been placed already.

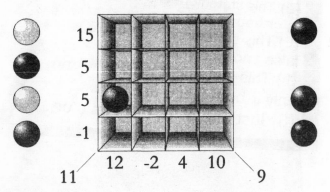

 Solve this additional puzzle for 5 bonus points:

Suppose that the diagonals read 7 and 7 (instead of the current 9 and 11) but the other figures remained the same. What would the position of the balls be now?

Puzzle 6	IN PERSPECTIVE	Points 2

Can you work out which word is being displayed in this picture?

Lateral Larry is looking at the chessboard below.
"Looks like someone was playing a game earlier,"
he says. "Hey, after the very next move one player
was checkmated. The thing is, I can't tell whether it
was White or Black."

To win this puzzle, explain why Larry couldn't say
who lost.

EVEN-ING ALL

The stall holder, Mandy Math, gives you seven disks. Each one bears a different number, from 0 to 6 inclusive. To win the game, place the disks in the engraved circles so that every straight line of 3 circles has an odd total.

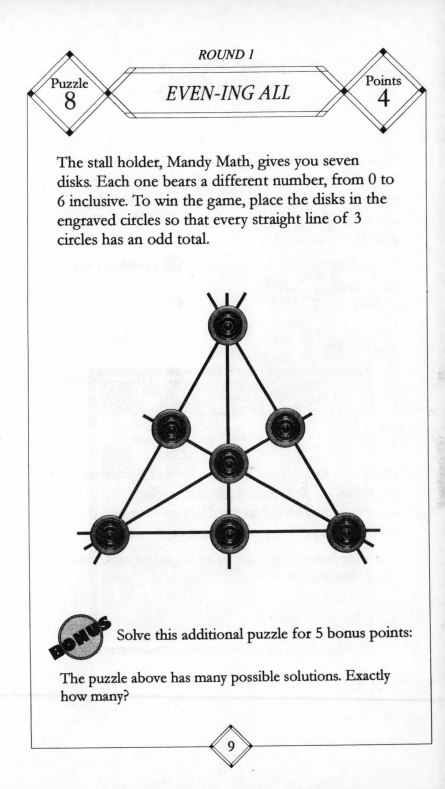

BONUS Solve this additional puzzle for 5 bonus points:

The puzzle above has many possible solutions. Exactly how many?

You enter the Verbal Vault and see this diagram on the wall:

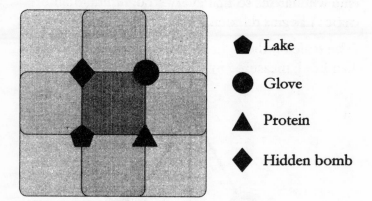

Lake

Glove

Protein

Hidden bomb

The four clues are all 4-letter words. They all start in the middle square and go around the corresponding shape in the diagram (not necessarily in the same direction each time).

The nine letters can then be arranged to make one word. What is it?

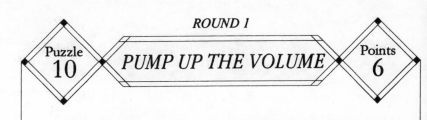

Mystic Molly has been constructing a store, made from connected tubes, to contain her special magic potion. Can you tell her how many units of potion she will be able to store in this contraption before tube A begins to overflow?

The scale on the right shows how much one tube can hold, measured in units.

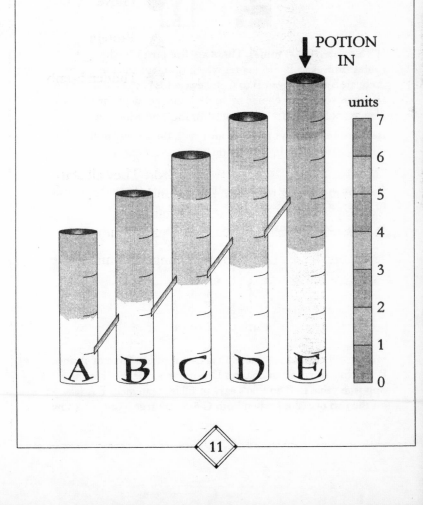

POTION
IN

units

7

6

5

4

3

2

1

0

A B C D E

ANSWERS

1. The answers are: (3) ANT, (4) EACH, (5) VENUE, (6) MAMMAL, (7) SEXTANT and (8) HOLOGRAM.

2. $200 is the least possible. Although it appears he should pay $300 for the signs (two lots of $100 and ten lots of $10), the carnival owner cleverly spotted that the same sign could be used for either direction, like so:

3. There are 10,000 routes. There are five possible, shortest routes from A to B. No matter which route we took to get to B, there are 5 routes from B to C. Likewise for C to D and D to A. In other words, our choice of route is independent for each leg. Hence 5 × 5 × 5 × 5 = 625 routes for the whole journey.

As there are ten ways to get from 1 to 2, the answer to the puzzle is 10 × 10 × 10 × 10 by the same reasoning.

4. As we don't know anything about A, B and C's truth, we need to consider all eight cases. Let's draw up a table:

Statement A	B	C	D	E	F	G
f	f	f	f	t	t	f
f	f	t	f	t	f	t ←
f	t	f	t	f	t	f
f	t	t	t	f	t	f
t	f	f	t	t	t	f
t	f	t	t	t	f	f
t	t	f	t	f	t	f
t	t	t	t	f	t	f

Here, t = True and f = False. D is true if at least one of A and B are true, so we fill in column D using this rule. E takes the opposite value to B so that's easy to fill in. Statement F is false on the two occasions when both C & E are true. Now we know statement G is true, and so we require only one of D, E and F to be true. This only happens in the second row. So we now know that A is false, B is false and C is true. Hence we can deduce that Jack doesn't have blond hair, Keith is under 6 feet tall and Laura is 23 years old.

5. It is obvious that the white ball must go at the bottom of the second column. The yellow ball must also go in the second column. The bottom row will either be White + Red + Yellow or White + Green to make up the -1. However, as the yellow and white balls cannot occupy the same space, it must be White + Green. Now for the top row, 15 = 7 + 6 + 2 or 6 + 4 + 3 + 2 are our only options (can't be 7 + 5 + 3 as the blue ball is in the third row). But we know the 3 point Green ball is on the bottom row, so we must have Black, Pink and Yellow here. Continuing this process, we arrive at the final answer (left):

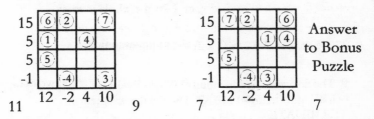

15 ⑥ ②   ⑦
5 ①   ④
5 ⑤
-1   ⑷   ③
    12 -2 4 10
11   9

15 ⑦ ②   ⑥
5   ① ④
5 ⑤
-1   ⑷ ③
    12 -2 4 10
7   7

Answer to Bonus Puzzle

6. The word is FORESHORTEN. Foreshortening is the effect whereby small objects look larger when they are close to you.

7. If black were to play the next move, moving the queen onto the same rank as white's king would mean white loses. However, suppose Larry was looking at the board upside-down. This is possible, since there is still a white square at the bottom-right as required. In this case, white is playing up the board so he can promote his pawn to a queen if his turn is next and thus checkmate black's king. See the diagram overleaf:

(7 contd.)

8. In 0 to 6, there are only three odd numbers. So, by ensuring one odd number lies on each path, the totals of all six lines will be odd. In other words, place the odd numbers on the shaded circles:

There are $(4 \times 3 \times 2) \times (3 \times 2) = 144$ possible solutions.

9. The answers are: (diamond) MINE, (circle) MITT, (pentagon) MERE and (triangle) MEAT. The 9-letter anagram is TERMINATE.

10. Molly could store 21 units of potion.

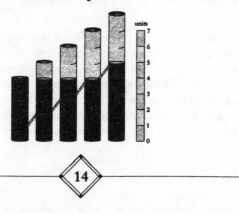

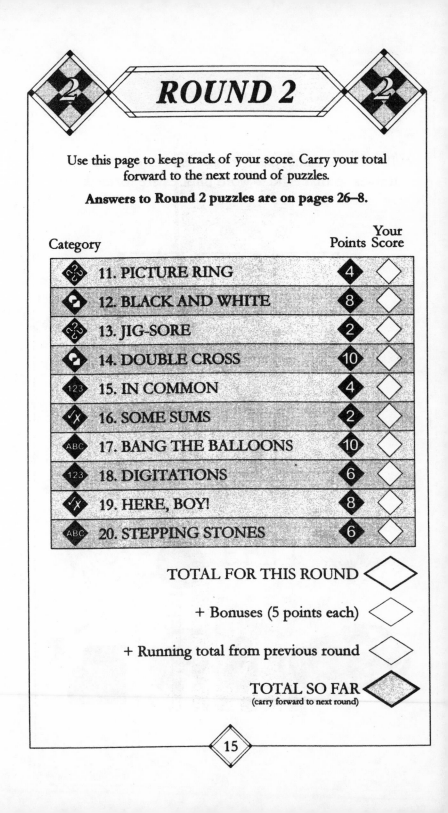

ROUND 2

Use this page to keep track of your score. Carry your total forward to the next round of puzzles.

Answers to Round 2 puzzles are on pages 26–8.

Category	Points	Your Score
11. PICTURE RING	4	◇
12. BLACK AND WHITE	8	◇
13. JIG-SORE	2	◇
14. DOUBLE CROSS	10	◇
15. IN COMMON	4	◇
16. SOME SUMS	2	◇
17. BANG THE BALLOONS	10	◇
18. DIGITATIONS	6	◇
19. HERE, BOY!	8	◇
20. STEPPING STONES	6	◇

TOTAL FOR THIS ROUND ◇

+ Bonuses (5 points each) ◇

+ Running total from previous round ◇

TOTAL SO FAR ◆
(carry forward to next round)

15

To win the game, place the pictures in the correct
frames so that eight 2-word phrases are formed.

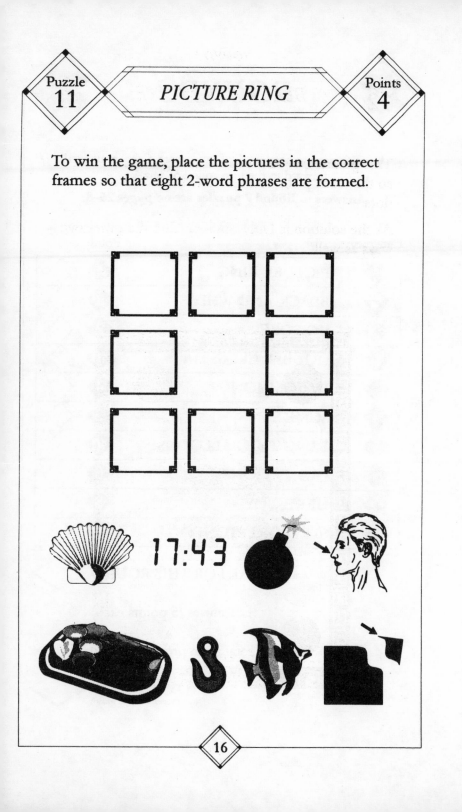

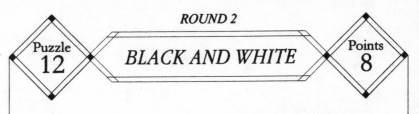

Puzzle
12

BLACK AND WHITE

Points
8

This picture can be divided into eight equal pieces so that each piece contains one black and two white dots.

As the solution is fairly obvious, find the other two ways as well.

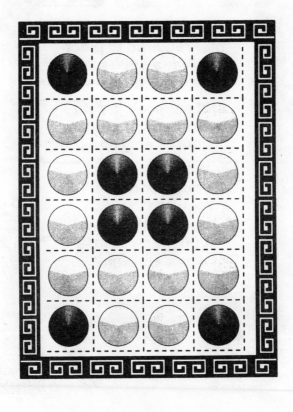

Solve the puzzle below.

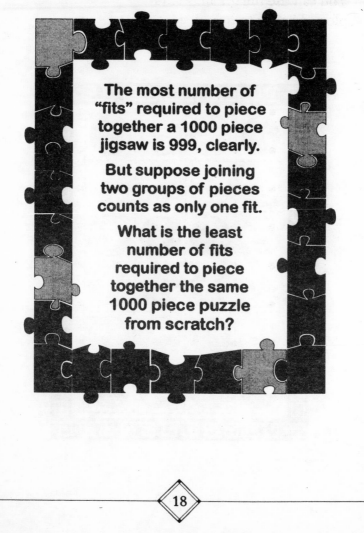

The most number of
"fits" required to piece
together a 1000 piece
jigsaw is 999, clearly.

But suppose joining
two groups of pieces
counts as only one fit.

What is the least
number of fits
required to piece
together the same
1000 piece puzzle
from scratch?

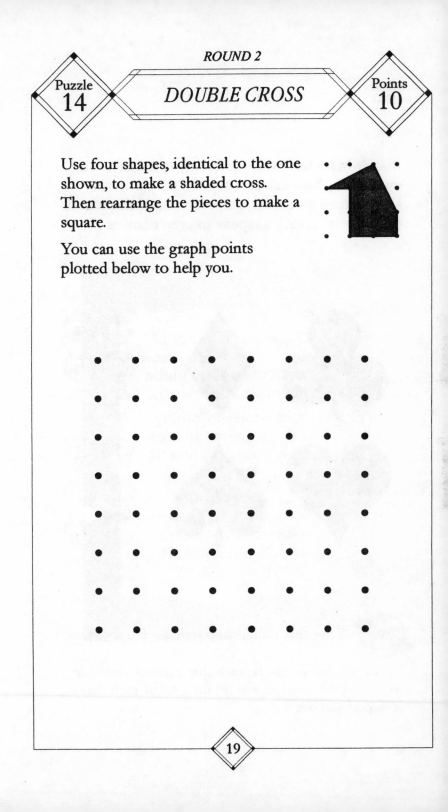

DOUBLE CROSS

Use four shapes, identical to the one shown, to make a shaded cross.
Then rearrange the pieces to make a square.

You can use the graph points plotted below to help you.

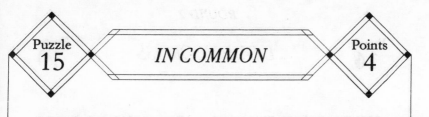

Mandy Math has twelve counters, as shown. You
must place three in each shape so that (a) each
shape shares a number with every other shape, and
(b) the total in each shape is an even number.

 Solve this additional puzzle for 5 bonus points:

Find a solution so that (a) each shape shares a number
with every other shape, and (b) the total of each shape
is an odd number.

Puzzle 15

IN COMMON

Points 4

Puzzle 15 — IN COMMON — Points 4

Mandy Math has twelve counters, as shown. You must place three in each shape so that (a) each shape shares a number with every other shape, and (b) the total in each shape is an even number.

Solve this additional puzzle for 5 bonus points:

Find a solution so that (a) each shape shares a number with every other shape, and (b) the total of each shape is an odd number.

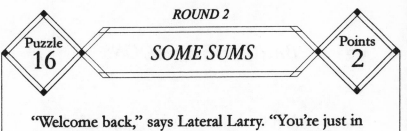

"Welcome back," says Lateral Larry. "You're just in time to try out my new game. Here are five tiles, each with symbols on them. You have to rearrange the tiles so that four correct calculations are formed. In order to win the game you must touch the fewest tiles possible."

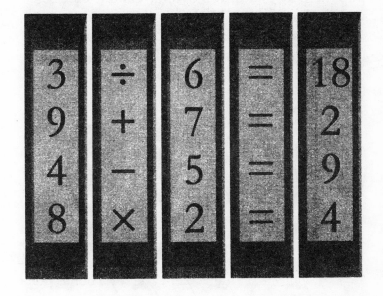

"Take a look at the balloons below," says Sideshow Sid. "As you can see, there is one letter on each of four white and four black balloons. I want you to burst the balloons in the order dictated by the rules to win the prize."

RULES:

(1) The black balloons should be popped in alphabetical order. (2) Don't start with the white A but, whenever you do pop this balloon, you must pop the C as your next move. (3) On one occasion, you need to pop two black balloons in a row. (4) Don't pop the I until two black balloons remain. (5) Once you have popped the final white balloon (which is not C or R), there should be one black balloon left.

DIGITATIONS

Shade in six of the white segments and place a mathematical sign in the circle so that a correct calculation is formed. The digits from 0 to 9 look like the following:

0 1 2 3 4 5 6 7 8 9

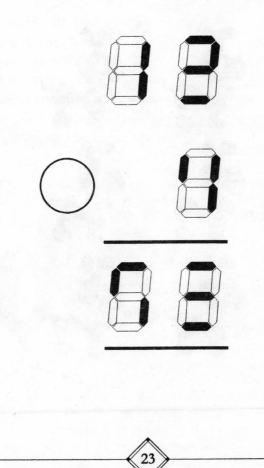

The six dogs below are walked around the carnival in pairs every day. How is it possible to arrange it so that no two dogs walk together more than once over a period of five days?

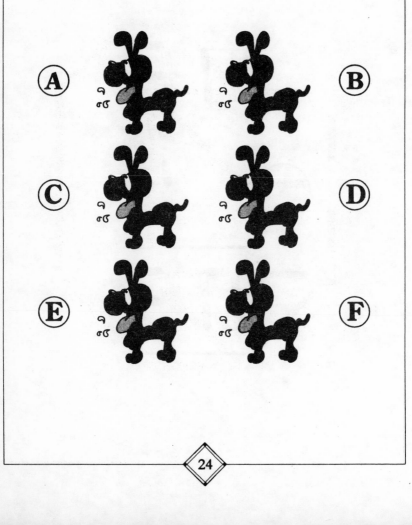

Puzzle 20

STEPPING STONES

Points 6

There are two words that can be made from the letters G, H, I, L, N, S, T and U. Place them in the grid so that either word can be spelled out by moving from circle to circle. Two letters have already been placed for you.

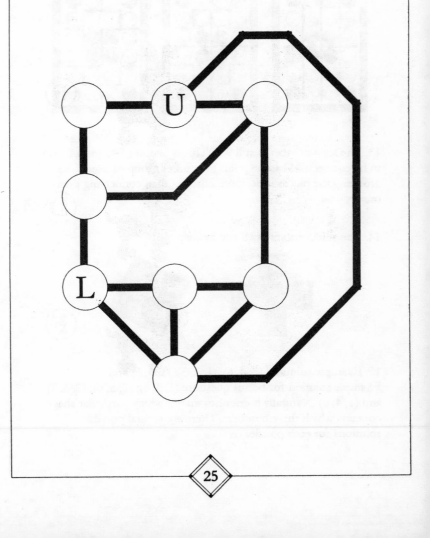

11. The eight boxes make a circle of phrases, as follows: Nose-piece, piece-meal, meal-time, time-bomb, bomb-shell, shell-fish, fish-hook, hook-nose.

12. The obvious and not-so-obvious solutions are shown here:

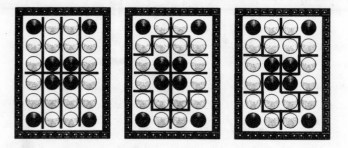

13. The least number is still 999. This is because 999 pieces have to be connected at some point to another group of pieces, so grouping the pieces is no more efficient than connecting them one-by-one.

14. The solutions are as shown below:

15. Example solution: (2, 4, 6); (1, 2, 3); (1, 4, 5) and (3, 5, 6). Example solution for bonus question: (1, 3, 5); (2, 5, 6); (2, 3, 4) and (1, 4, 6). Naturally it does not matter which particular shape contains which three numbers. There are several possible solutions for each puzzle.

ANSWERS

16. Just one – turn the second tile upside-down:

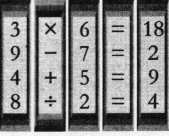

3	×	6	=	18
9	–	7	=	2
4	+	5	=	9
8	÷	2	=	4

17. By rules 1 and 5, V must be the last balloon to be popped, and N or the white A is the penultimate balloon. By rules 1 and 4, the I must be the fourth balloon, and the second and third balloons are white. Therefore, the black A is the first balloon and (by rule 3) we now know the fifth balloon must be the L. This gives us the following position:

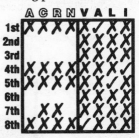

The white A can't be third because the C needs to be in position 4 to satisfy rule 2, but this slot is already filled. It cannot be sixth or seventh for similar reasons. So it must be in position 2 and the C is third. The N is the only remaining possibility for the seventh balloon, leaving R in position 6. So the final order goes: black A, white A, C, I, L, R, N, V.

18. 13 X 4 = 52.

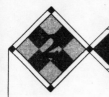
19. One possible solution is shown below:

Day 1 AB CD EF
Day 2 AC BE DF
Day 3 AD BF CE
Day 4 AE BD CF
Day 5 AF BC DE

20. The two words are SUNLIGHT and HUSTLING. Once you have worked this out, you know that the N must be connected to U and L (because of the way SUNLIGHT is spelt) and must also be next to I and G (so HUSTLING can be spelt). So N must be connected to four letters and hence must appear in the bottom circle. You can likewise conclude that S need only be connected to U and T, and hence must appear in the top-left circle. This, coupled with the two letters you are given to begin with, yields the following solution:

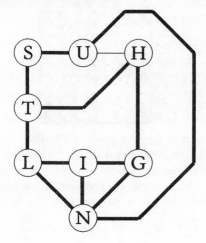

ROUND 3

Use this page to keep track of your score. Carry your total forward to the next round of puzzles.

Answers to Round 3 puzzles are on pages 40–2.

Category	Points	Your Score
21. 3 RING CIRCUS	4	◇
22. ABOUT LAST KNIGHT...	4	◇
23. PENNY PUSH	6	◇
24. OVERTYPE	8	◇
25. WHEEL OF FORTUNE	6	◇
26. GET OUT CLAUSE	10	◇
27. TREASURE ISLAND	10	◇
28. SQUARE DEAL	2	◇
29. EITHER WAY	2	◇
30. STAIRCASE SEQUENCE	8	◇

TOTAL FOR THIS ROUND ◇

+ Bonuses (5 points each) ◇

+ Running total from previous round ◇

TOTAL SO FAR ◆
(carry forward to next round)

Place the numbers 1 to 9 in the spaces (using each digit only once) so that (a) the three numbers on all the rings add up to 15, and (b) the three numbers between each pair of like arrows add up to 15.

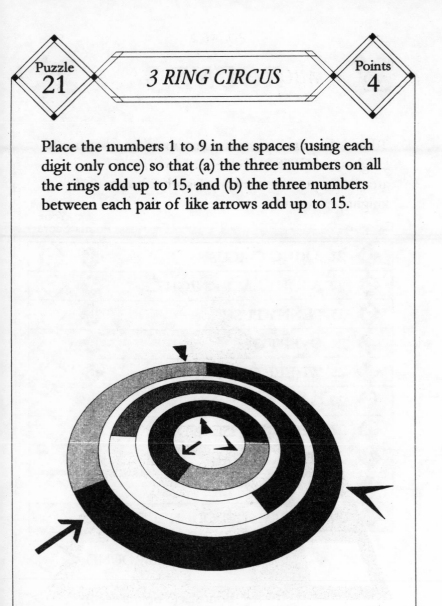

ABOUT LAST KNIGHT...

To win the game, place the maximum number of knights on the 5×5 chessboard so that no knight attacks a square occupied by another knight. One knight per square!

PENNY PUSH

A move consists of sliding a penny along a plank to
the empty space. You have nine moves to rearrange
the coins so that they read clockwise from 1 to 6,
starting with 1 in the top-left corner.

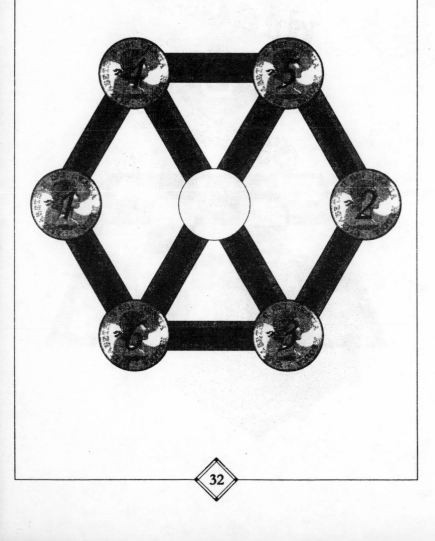

Puzzle
24

OVERTYPE

Points
8

Four pairs of words have been overtyped. What are they?

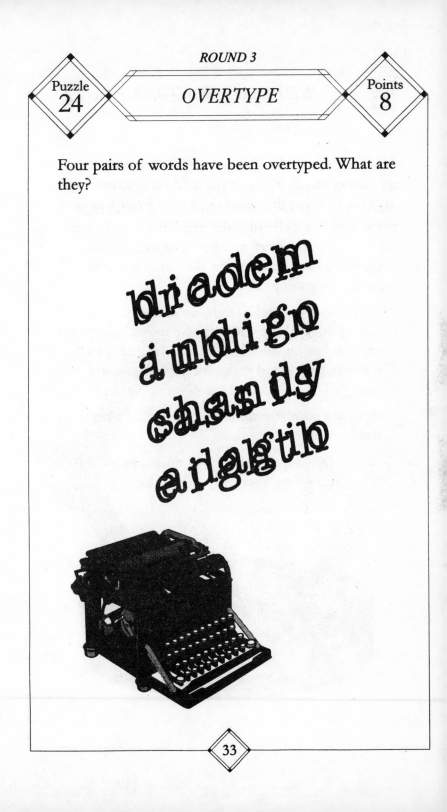

Mandy Math works as a croupier in a casino.

There are 42 numbers on her roulette wheel. Starting at 0, if she counts every third number on the wheel, she finds that she gets back to 0 before she has counted every number. The same thing happens if she counts every 14th or every 21st number, for example.

Mandy wants a wheel so that, no matter what counting interval she chooses, she will always visit every number on the wheel before returning to 0. She thinks this would make for a fairer roulette wheel.

How many numbers should be on such a wheel? Choose from:

(a) 43 numbers; (b) 44 numbers;
(c) 45 numbers; (d) 46 numbers?

GET OUT CLAUSE

To win the game you must pass through the maze. Unfortunately, there are a number of locked passages (represented by the boxes). There are six keys, each of which opens all the doors bearing that symbol. You are allowed to take three keys — which three would allow you to win?

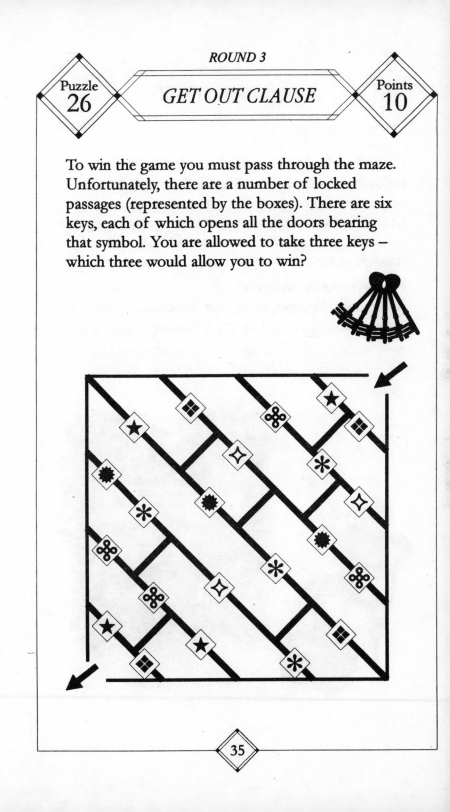

Pirate Pete knows six things. (a) One of the
following statements is false; (b) The treasure is not
on a main diagonal; (c) The treasure is not in row
C; (d) The treasure is not in an even-numbered
column; (e) The treasure is not in D3; (f) The
treasure is not in a corner.

He can't deduce which of (b) to (f) is the false
statement. However, using this information what is
his probability of finding the treasure?

	1	2	3	4
A				
B				
C				
D				

SQUARE DEAL

"I'll make you this deal," says Mandy Math, holder of the Number Cruncher stall at the carnival. "In the equation below, the same number must be placed in each box. You can win your points for this game if you can tell me all the numbers that can fit in the squares."

A bystander offers the answer "Seven".

"Too bad, you lose," says Mandy.

Can you see the trick behind Mandy's swindle and thus provide the correct answer?

$$(\square \times \square) - \square = 42$$

EITHER WAY

Can you spot 18 words of four letters or more that have something in common? The words read in any direction.

```
T S O M N S G U S R L B
N B O O B H M A D A M R
O R L L C A T J E D I O
W T E I O H K E N A N T
Z Q V F G S R P N R I A
C I E M E O G E E E M V
C P L X T R S I D D T A
P O E O K T E E S D G T
M S R E O Y E S A M E O
O P O O P D S A G Q E R
W F T T F S F K A Y A K
N O O N W T H O S J O Q
```

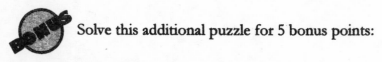 Solve this additional puzzle for 5 bonus points:

To claim the bonus, name all 23 words.

STAIRCASE SEQUENCE

Work out the logic behind this sequence. To win the game you must say on which step the numbers 49 and 122 would be placed.

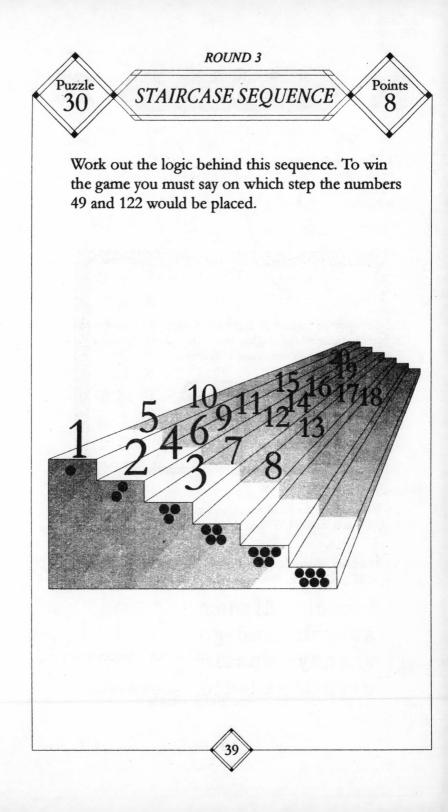

21. The trick is to realize that it is the classic "15 Magic Square" puzzle but with the ends joined to make circles instead of rows and columns:

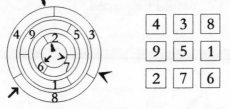

4	3	8
9	5	1
2	7	6

22. The most is thirteen. You can place a knight on all the white squares because all the knights would then attack the black squares, as shown in this example illustration:

23. Move 5 into the blank space, and continue with coins 4, 1, 6, 5, 4, 2, 3 and finally 4. (Other solutions exist.)

24. The pairs of words are as shown. The first letters also spell out ACID and BASE, two more related words.

brooch   diadem
auburn   indigo
shandy   cassis
eighth   adagio   (musical terms)

ANSWERS

25. 43 numbers (option (a)) would be the best by far. Because 43 is a prime number, and hence has no smaller prime factors, Mandy can't avoid cycling through every number.

26. The ◈, ✦, and ✳ keys are used. The trick is to realize that you have to go backwards in order to go forwards:

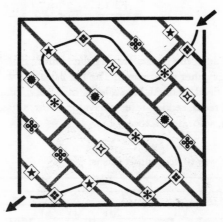

27. If statement (b) is false (and hence the rest are true) then the treasure must be in B3. If (c) is false, it must be C1. If (d) is false, all the locations are discounted except for A2, B4 and D2. If (e) is false, the treasure must surely be in D3! Statement (f) cannot be false because if so then (b) must be true, but these two contradict one another. So, even if you don't know which of (b) to (f) is the false statement, you can narrow your odds to 6-in-16 (or 3-in-8) since there are six out of the 16 squares left.

28. Mandy asked for "*all* the numbers that can fit in the squares". Seven is a correct answer, but -6 works also:

$$(\boxed{-6} \times \boxed{-6}) - \boxed{-6} = 42$$

(28 contd.)

For those of you familiar with quadratic equations, the clever way of working it out goes like this:

$$x^2 - x - 42 = 0$$

$$x = \frac{1 \pm \sqrt{1 + (4 \times 1 \times 42)}}{2}$$

$$= \frac{1 \pm 13}{2} = 7 \text{ or } -6$$

29. The words in the puzzle are all palindromes, making it twice as easy as any other wordsearch! The full list of 23 words is: boob, civic, deed, denned, kayak, level, madam, minim, noon, peep, poop, radar, redder, refer, rotavator, rotor, sagas, sees, sexes, shahs, solos, tenet, toot.

30. A better way of looking at this is:

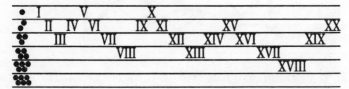

Hence 49 = XLIX = 4 symbols, hence goes on the 4th step down. Likewise, 122 = CXXII = 5 symbols, so goes on the 5th step down.

ROUND 4

Use this page to keep track of your score. Carry your total forward to the next round of puzzles.

Answers to Round 4 puzzles are on pages 54–6.

Category	Points	Your Score
ABC 31. LETTER BOX	6	◇
32. PEN PUZZLE	4	◇
ABC 33. TRIGRAPHS	6	◇
34. IT'S A DEAL	10	◇
35. "I'LL LAND" A JOB	2	◇
123 36. BRIGHT SPARK	8	◇
37. BOX SQUASH	2	◇
38. ANIMAL ANTICS	4	◇
123 39. GOLDEN GAMBLE	10	◇
ABC 40. WHICH PRIZE?	8	◇

TOTAL FOR THIS ROUND ◇

+ Bonuses (5 points each) ◇

+ Running total from previous round ◇

TOTAL SO FAR ◇
(carry forward to next round)

LETTER BOX

Place the letters in the grid so that a 16-letter word can be read counterclockwise in spiral fashion. To give you a clue, the letters appear in the corresponding column or row. For example, R and L appear somewhere in the first column.

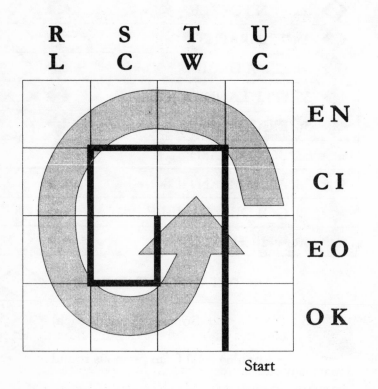

Start

PEN PUZZLE

Use three wooden pens of the same shape (but not necessarily the same size) so that all the sheep are separate from one another and can't escape. The pens may not overlap.

Solve this additional puzzle for 5 bonus points:

How many circular fences would you need to ensure that the sheep are separated and can't escape? Overlapping is allowed here.

The following words are in the Verbal Vault for a special reason – they are the only words with the following combinations of three letters. Using the clues, can you say what the words are?

CLUES
(in no particular order)

Listening equipment

Shelves

Wavy

Dinner jacket

Flexible

Baby bird

IT'S A DEAL

Marvin the Magician baffles many passers-by at his Mystery Box stall. Today he is showing his audience a card trick.

"I have thirteen cards in my hand. As you can see, they are mixed at random." He shows the cards to the audience who confirm that they don't seem to be in any particular order.

"I will now spell out the cards in sequence," says Marvin. "First we have the Ace, so I shall spell out A, C, E!" Holding the pack face down, he takes a card from the top of the deck and deals it to the bottom for the "A", likewise for the "C" and on the count of "E" he takes the next card from the top of the deck and deals it face up onto the table. It is indeed the Ace.

He then counts "T, W, O!" and again the third card is dealt onto the table to show a Two. He continues through the cards, dealing the cards in order until he has the King left in his hand.

How could you stack the cards to repeat this trick without using sleight of hand?

"I'LL LAND" A JOB

An unemployed businessman travels to an island.
He would desperately like a job, but the island is
uninhabited and no ships ever pass by.

However, it was only a matter of hours before he
got an interview for a good management job. He
started work the next day.

How come?

BRIGHT SPARK

Adept types can try their luck at the shooting stall. Punters have six shots, one for each of the six targets. On average, the chance of someone hitting the target is 50% each time. A light is lit for every hit target.

Mandy Math runs side bets on what will happen in the next game. People bet on whether there will be an even number (i.e. 0, 2, 4 or 6) or odd number (i.e. 1, 3 or 5) of lights at the end of the six shots. She offers even money on either gamble.

Providing fair play is assured, which of the two bets provides the better odds, or are they equally good?

What word can be read here?

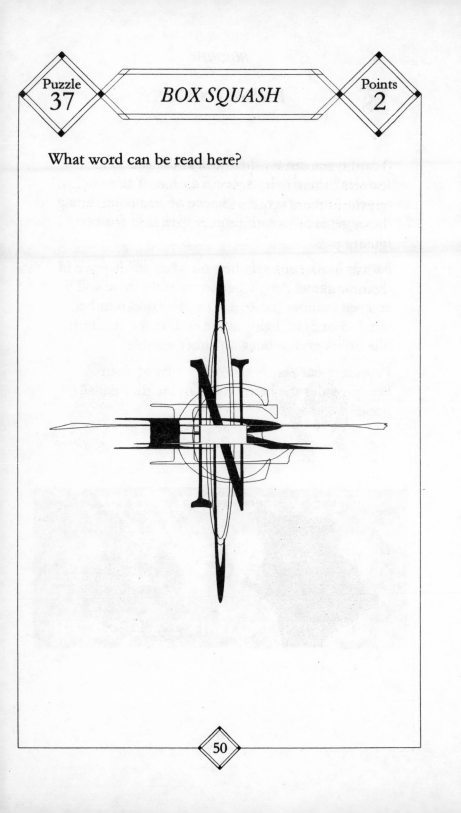

ANIMAL ANTICS

For the amusement of younger visitors to the carnival, there is an Animals Corner. The variety of creatures there is quite impressive, including koala bears, silkworms, prairie dogs, jackrabbits and guinea pigs.

What, in particular, do these five creatures have in common?

Mandy Math offers you this gamble:

"Take a normal, two-sided coin. Toss it. If it turns up heads, you get $2. If it is tails but heads on the next throw, you get $4. If it is tails, then tails, then heads on the third throw, you get $8. Tails, tails, tails, heads gains you $16, and so on."

"So," she concludes, "if you get a tail the amount doubles and you toss again; if you get a head, the game stops and you collect your winnings."

What is the largest amount of money you would be prepared to pay to play this game?

WHICH PRIZE?

Will the Wordsmith has four prizes on offer in his stall, but only one is valuable. Complete the puzzle, then deduce whether you'd choose the pearl necklace, the gold bar, the diamonds or the oil painting. One clue has been filled in for you.

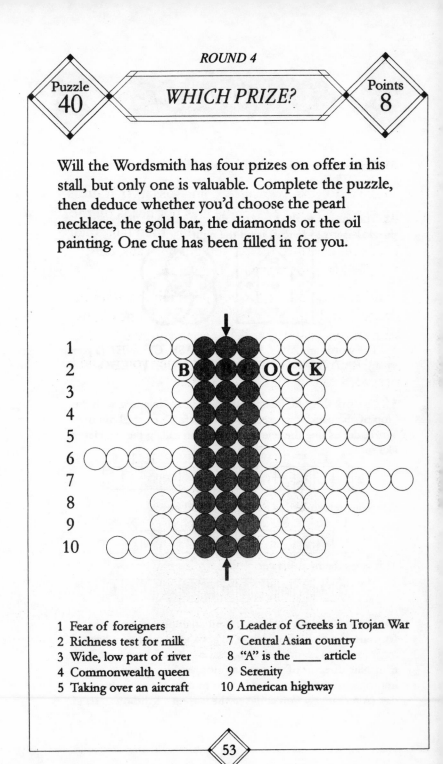

1 Fear of foreigners
2 Richness test for milk
3 Wide, low part of river
4 Commonwealth queen
5 Taking over an aircraft
6 Leader of Greeks in Trojan War
7 Central Asian country
8 "A" is the _____ article
9 Serenity
10 American highway

31. The word is, appropriately enough, COUNTER-CLOCKWISE!

32. The answer to the main puzzle is shown left; the bonus puzzle answer (4 fences) is on the right.

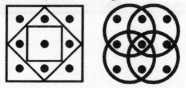

33. The words are ZIGZAG, BOOKCASE, CYGNET (a young swan), EASYGOING, HEADPHONES and TUXEDO.

34. To work this out, imagine thirteen boxes in a row, with the "top of the pack" represented on the left. Then spell out the words, depositing the relevant card upon calling the final letter, like so:

A C E T W O T H R E E F O

| | A | | 2 | | | | | 3 | | |

Continue, remembering to skip the filled boxes:

U R F I V E S I X S

| 4 | A | | 2 | | 5 | | 3 | 6 |

This gives the final answer:

Top of pack: Q 4 A 8 K 2 7 5 10 J 3 6 9

35. This is based on a true story. An unemployed executive, frustrated by fruitless attempts to get a job, stood on a busy *traffic* (or *safety*) island with a sign saying "Can I have a job?" The managing director of a company stopped his car and, after an impromptu interview, asked him to turn up for a job the next day. (Alternatively, you could say he was on a lighthouse island.)

ANSWERS

36. You'd think that the "even numbers" bet would be slightly better, because there are four outcomes (0, 2, 4, 6) rather than the three odd numbers (1, 3, 5). However, one has to take into account how many possible ways there are of scoring each number of lights:

No. of ways 0 lights lit = 1
No. of ways 1 light lit = 6
No. of ways 2 lights lit = 15
No. of ways 3 lights lit = 20
No. of ways 4 lights lit = 15
No. of ways 5 lights lit = 6
No. of ways 6 lights lit = 1

The number of ways an even number of lights could be shown is therefore 1 + 15 + 15 + 1 = 32. The total for the odd numbers is 6 + 20 + 6 = 32. Hence, the bets are equally likely.

37. The word is CONCERT. A very tall, thin C can be read, followed by O, N, then a fairly normal C and E, followed by a very short and wide R and T.

38. All the animals are "misnomers" as their names don't describe what they actually are. A silkworm is not a worm, it is a larva; a jackrabbit is a hare; a koala "bear" is a marsupial; and prairie dogs and guinea pigs are classified as rodents, rather than dogs and pigs.

39. Theoretically one should pay as high a price as necessary, even all the money there is in the world. To work out the fair price for a game such as this, mathematicians use something called the "expectation". The expectation is equal to the probability of an outcome multiplied by its reward, summed over all the outcomes possible. In this instance:

$$\text{Expectation} = \text{Probability} \times \text{Reward}$$
$$\text{Exp. for H} = \tfrac{1}{2} \times \ \ \$2 = \$1$$
$$\text{Exp. for T, H} = \tfrac{1}{4} \times \ \ \$4 = \$1$$
$$\text{Exp. for T, T, H} = \tfrac{1}{8} \times \ \ \$8 = \$1$$
$$\text{Exp. for T, T, T, H} = \tfrac{1}{16} \times \$16 = \$1$$
$$\text{etc.}$$

So the expectation for the gamble is the total of these, namely $1+$1+$1+$1+$1+... which is an infinite amount. Hence offering **any** finite amount of money would be too cheap.

40. All the letters in the shaded squares are consecutive in the alphabet. The arrowed column reads OBTAIN GEMS so you should have opted for the diamonds.

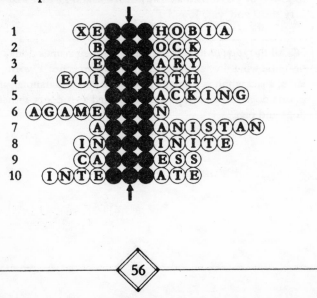

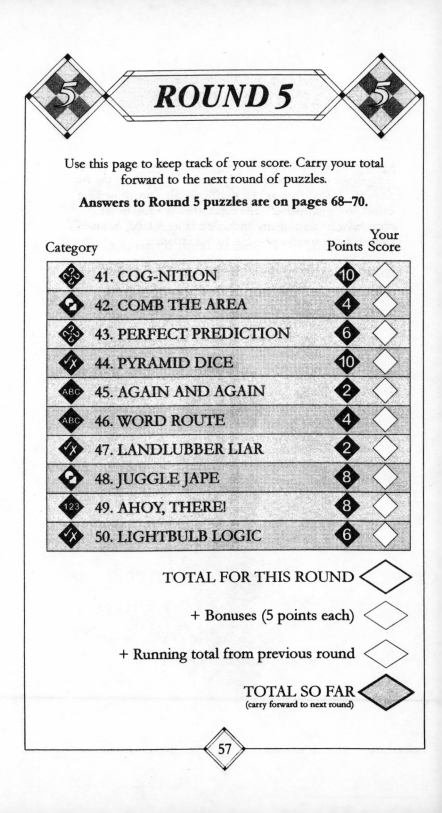

ROUND 5

Use this page to keep track of your score. Carry your total forward to the next round of puzzles.

Answers to Round 5 puzzles are on pages 68–70.

Category	Points	Your Score
41. COG-NITION	10	◇
42. COMB THE AREA	4	◇
43. PERFECT PREDICTION	6	◇
44. PYRAMID DICE	10	◇
45. AGAIN AND AGAIN	2	◇
46. WORD ROUTE	4	◇
47. LANDLUBBER LIAR	2	◇
48. JUGGLE JAPE	8	◇
49. AHOY, THERE!	8	◇
50. LIGHTBULB LOGIC	6	◇

TOTAL FOR THIS ROUND ◇

+ Bonuses (5 points each) ◇

+ Running total from previous round ◇

TOTAL SO FAR ◆
(carry forward to next round)

Mystic Molly owns four pieces of semiprecious onyx which she uses to predict events. They have holes through the middle so that they interlock like cogs when placed on spindles. The O, N, Y and X cogs have 13, 14, 15 and 16 teeth respectively.

How many times does the N cog need to be rotated before the word ONYX is displayed correctly again?

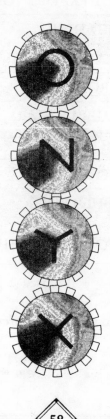

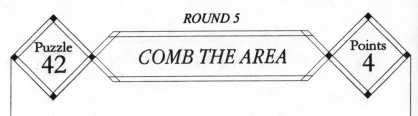

COMB THE AREA

The Animals Corner at the carnival also contains an apiary. One particular bee is trying to collect honey for the queen. He wants to start from empty cell S, then collect three cells worth of honey, then have a rest on an empty cell, then collect three cells, then rest again, and so on until he reaches F.

Which route should the bee take in order to collect all the honey?

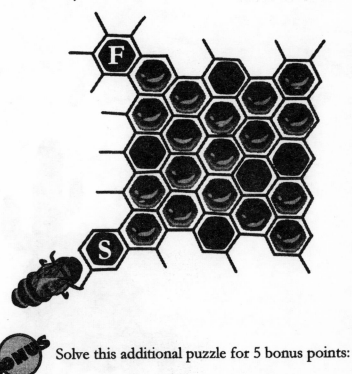

BONUS Solve this additional puzzle for 5 bonus points:

There are two possible solutions – find the other one.

PERFECT PREDICTION

Tex the Mex was having a siesta in a sunny corner of the fairground when he thought up the astonishing sentence below. Clearly the statement was true, as there were seven mentions of "one", three mentions of "two" and so on.

A very similar sentence can be made by changing some of the numbers in bold type. Can you work out how to do it?

I predict there are **7** 1s, **3** 2s, **2** 3s, **1** 4, **1** 5, **1** 6, **2** 7s, **1** 8, and **1** 9 in this sentence.

PYRAMID DICE

"Here's a challenge for you," teases Wordsmith Will. "No matter how I roll these three tetrahedra, that's four-sided dice to you and me, I can almost always make a word from the letters that touch the table when they land."

He tosses the dice eight times, and makes the following words:

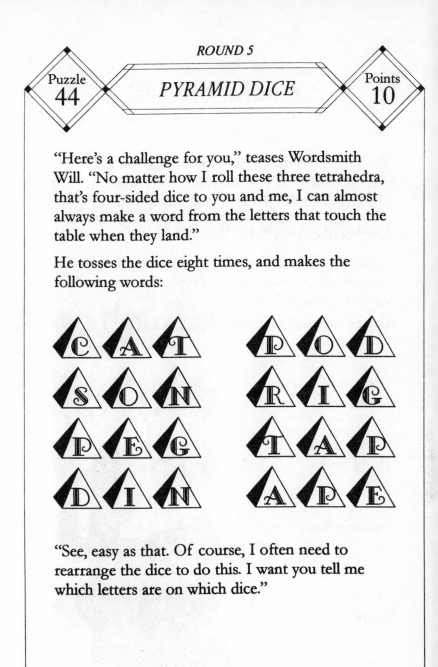

"See, easy as that. Of course, I often need to rearrange the dice to do this. I want you tell me which letters are on which dice."

AGAIN AND AGAIN

You must find the five 6-letter words, using the clues provided. If you are stuck, the phrase MUTANT DISHWATER might help you.

Then again, it might confuse you further.

Calcium deposit on teeth

Bullet that explodes on impact

Hergé's hero

Famous "Lord", traitor of WWII

Tropical fly, cause of sleeping sickness

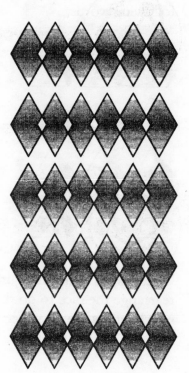

WORD ROUTE

Examine the three diagrams and decide what the
final diagram should like.

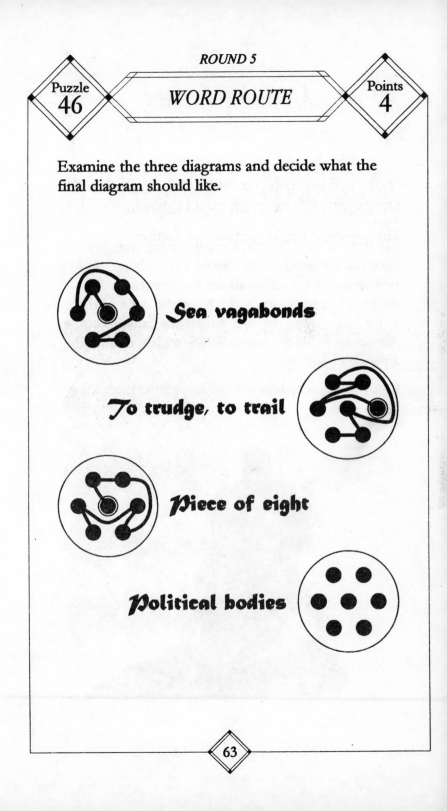

Sea vagabonds

To trudge, to trail

Piece of eight

Political bodies

Near the quayside end of the carnival a fisherman with weather-worn, suntanned skin is repairing his nets. "Ahoy, there!" he says. You ask him about his net.

"If it wasn't for this net I wouldn't be alive. My boat ran aground in the Pacific a month ago and I was stranded on an island for three weeks with nothing but my clothes, the boat, the net and the knife I use to gut the fish. I used the knife to cut up the net to form the letters S.O.S. which, thankfully, a passing plane spotted."

Can you see why this fisherman is (ahem) spinning you a yarn?

JUGGLE JAPE

Jeremy Jester, one of the most popular clowns in the carnival's circus, was pondering on a problem. He placed one of his juggling balls inside a ring then pushed the ball around inside it, keeping the ball in close contact all the way around one circuit of the ring.

How many times would you expect the juggling ball to rotate?

 Solve this additional puzzle for 5 bonus points:

How many times would the ball have revolved if it started on the **outside** of the ring?

Three lighthouses each make a sighting of a lost ship. What is the likelihood that the ship will be found in the sighting triangle formed?

Assume that each lighthouse is equally likely to miss to the left or right of the ship.

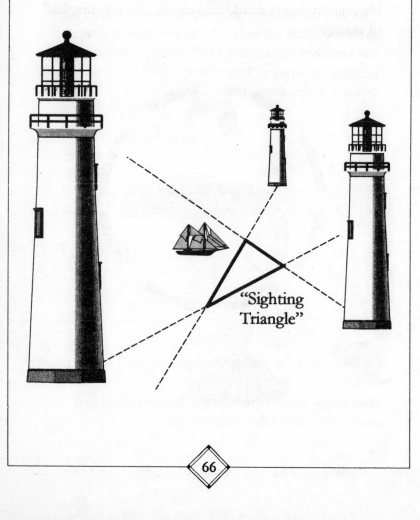

"Sighting Triangle"

LIGHTBULB LOGIC

Lateral Larry offers you a puzzle to tackle. "Here are three switches, one of which is connected to the lamp inside this sealed, black box. You are allowed to open the box once, but once you do so – that's it, no more switch presses because you've gotta tell me your answer."

"To win the game, you must tell me which of the three switches turns on the lamp." Given that all the switches are at the "off" position at the beginning, what strategy can you devise that ensures a win every time?

41. We need not bother about the O cog because it always looks like an O. The N cog has 14 teeth, but because it looks correct upside down it is correct every 7 teeth. The Y has 15 teeth but looks correct every 5 teeth. The X has 16 teeth but looks correct every 4 teeth. As 7, 5 and 4 have no common factors, we just multiply the numbers to get 140 teeth - that is, for every 140 teeth (or 140 / 14 = 10 turns) the N cog turns through, ONYX is again displayed. Hence the answer is 10.

42.

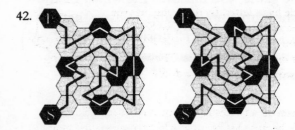

43. "I predict there will be **1** 0, **11** 1s, **2** 2s, **1** 3, **1** 4, **1** 5, **1** 6, **1** 7, **1** 8, and **1** 9 in this sentence." This is correct because there is one 0, eleven 1s, two 2s etc. in the whole sentence.

44. The general principle used throughout this puzzle is "If ABC is a word, and A is on die 1, then B and C must be on 2 and 3 or vice versa." Using the word CAT, let's say C is on 1, A is on 2, and T is on 3. Using PEG, TAP and APE readily gets us to this position:

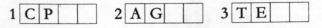

We have D, O, S, N, I and R left. By POD, O and D can't be on die 1. Similarly, RIG means R and I can't be on die 2. Now it gets tricky. If you try to place N on die 2 you find that DIN, SON and RIG can't all work, so this is impossible. Likewise, if you try to place N on die 3 you find that DIN, SON and POD

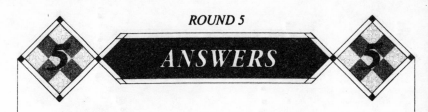

don't all work. Therefore, N must be on die 1. From now on it's easy to deduce the final answer:

1 | C | P | N | R | 2 | A | G | D | S | 3 | T | E | O | I |

45. The answers are TARTAR, DUMDUM, TINTIN, HAWHAW and TSETSE. The first three (or last three!) letters of each word together make up the phrase "mutant dishwater".

46. Each circle has a letter. By deducing that the previous clues refer to PIRATES, TRAIPSE and PIASTRE, you can work out that PARTIES looks like the diagram shown here. The first letter of the word is denoted by a double circle.

47. If he'd been on a Pacific island for three weeks, his chin would be pale because his beard would have prevented tanning.

48. By noting that the circumference of the ring is four times that of the ball, you'd think that the answer is four. However, the correct response is five. If we broke the ring and straightened it out, then the answer would be four, but the ball travelling around the ring causes an extra rotation. The answer to the bonus question is six.

49. One-in-four. Each of the three sightings can miss to the left or right, so there are $2 \times 2 \times 2 = 8$ possibilities. Of these, only two enclose the ship in the sighting triangle. These occur when all the sightings miss to the left (or to the right) of the ship, as shown:

50. Turn on switch 1. Leave it for five minutes to make the lamp hot. Then switch it off and turn on switch 2. Immediately open the box and feel the lamp. Using this method you can always win no matter which switch is connected to the lamp:

> If lamp is off and hot = switch 1.
> If lamp is on and cold = switch 2.
> If lamp is off and cold = switch 3.
> Lamp on and hot is not possible.

TEST YOUR STRENGTH

How are you doing? Calculate your score so far and see how high you can try ...

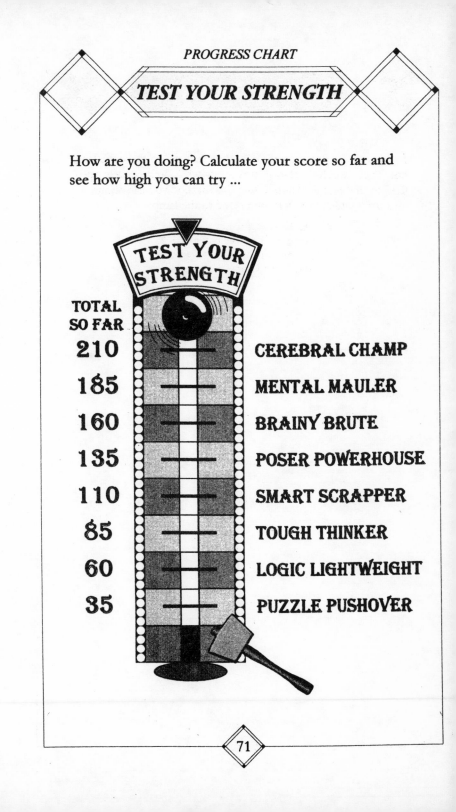

TOTAL SO FAR	
210	CEREBRAL CHAMP
185	MENTAL MAULER
160	BRAINY BRUTE
135	POSER POWERHOUSE
110	SMART SCRAPPER
85	TOUGH THINKER
60	LOGIC LIGHTWEIGHT
35	PUZZLE PUSHOVER

ROUND 6

Use this page to keep track of your score. Carry your total forward to the next round of puzzles.

Answers to Round 6 puzzles are on pages 84–6.

Category	Points	Your Score
51. INFINITY HOTEL	8	◇
52. HARDEN THE GARDEN	6	◇
53. FISHY BUSINESS	10	◇
54. TRIANGULATION	4	◇
55. LETTER LIFT	6	◇
56. SECOND THOUGHTS	2	◇
		◇
...N BASKETS	8	◇
59. THE SLEEPY CLOWN	4	◇
60. CRYPT-OLOGY	10	◇

TOTAL FOR THIS ROUND ◇

+ Bonuses (5 points each) ◇

+ Running total from previous round ◇

TOTAL SO FAR ◆
(carry forward to next round)

"So the story goes," Mystic Molly begins, "there is a ghostly hotel in the grounds of the carnival which has an infinite number of rooms. The place is so popular that it is always full. However, should a ghost want a room for the night the inn keeper would just ask the ghost in room 1 to move to room 2, the ghost in 2 to move to 3, and so on for all the rooms."

Despite your disbelief, she continues. "On Halloween night, an infinite number of ghosts came to stay. Can you tell me how he accommodated the spooks?"

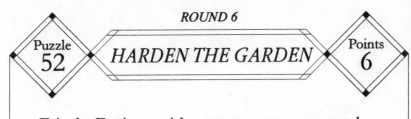

HARDEN THE GARDEN

Eric the Engineer wishes to concrete over a patch of waste land to make it into a good seating area for when the carnival's visitors want to take a break. The area is a trapezium in shape, and he thinks he can work out its area by the formula:

$$\frac{(a+b)}{2} \times h$$

Is this correct? If so, prove it. If not, what is the correct formula that Eric should use?

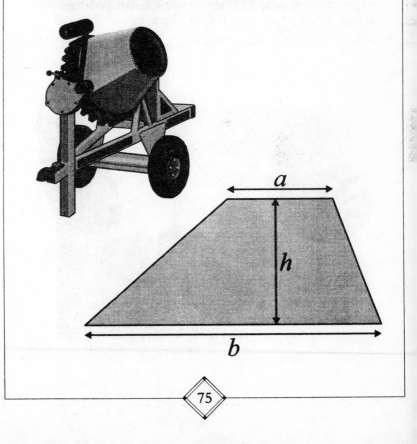

On the island of Zog, the traders use shells as a means of currency. A winkle shell is worth four clams. However, one nautilus shell is worth seven clams because it is more rare.

The disadvantage with this system is that, even if you have a very large supply of winkle and nautilus shells, it is impossible to buy something costing the equivalent of nine clams.

What is the total of all the numbers that are impossible to make up using winkles and nautiluses only?

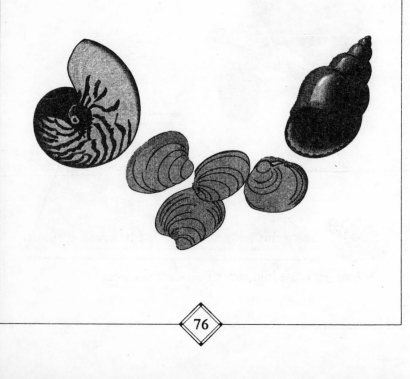

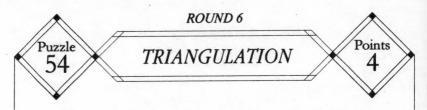

Puzzle
54

TRIANGULATION

Points
4

Visual Vern, the keeper of the Picture Palace stall, challenges you to one of his games. "Here is a triangle of cotton buds. Normally these puzzles use matchsticks, but my mother told me never to play with matches," he chuckles.

"Anyway, what you have to do is move four cotton buds in order to halve the area of the figure."

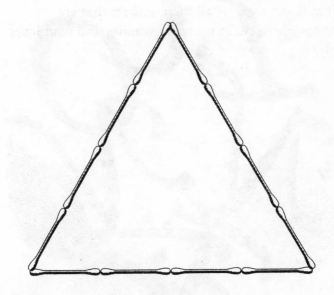

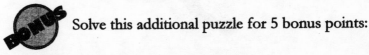
Solve this additional puzzle for 5 bonus points:

Move six buds instead, to quarter the area.

Which word can be made by picking up the letters
in sequence? That is, when lifting a letter you must
not disturb any of the letters underneath.

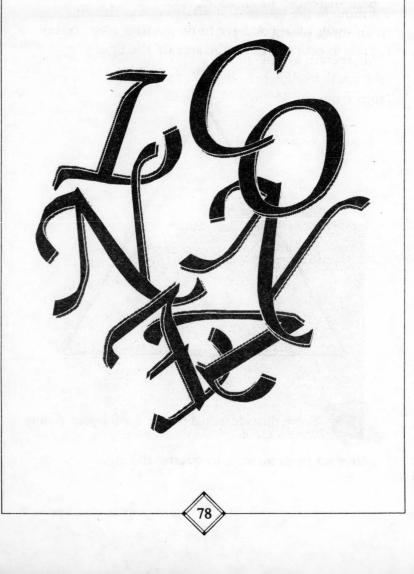

SECOND THOUGHTS

Lateral Larry shows you a postcard. "Here's where I went for my holidays last year. As you might know, it's only one of two objects that can be made out when looking at the Earth from the Moon."

"I thought the Great Wall of China was the only man-made object that could be seen," you say.

"Ah, therein lies the puzzle," says Larry. Apart from the Earth itself, what other object on Earth can be seen from the Moon with the naked eye?

TAKE A PICTURE

What animal would suitably fit in the blank box?

EGGS IN BASKETS

Mandy Math needs three boxes each containing a dozen eggs. She currently has three boxes containing 21, 9 and 6 eggs.

She would like to take three moves to complete the task, where a move consists of doubling the number of eggs by taking the required number from ONE other box.

How does she do it using exactly three moves?

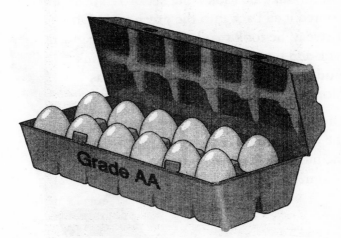

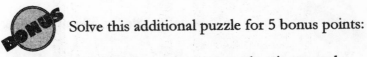 Solve this additional puzzle for 5 bonus points:

How does she perform the same task using exactly two moves?

Colin the Clown, one of the carnival entertainers, looks after two large tanks of paint which are used to make fairground signs. One of the tanks contains red paint, the other green.

Unfortunately, Colin has had a terrible week, because the other clown has been ill, and Colin has had to work so many extra hours he could hardly keep his eyes open. As a result, he has made a lot of silly mistakes.

On Monday, he took a bucket of red paint but poured it all back into the green tank. On Tuesday, he took two buckets from the green tank and poured it back into the red tank. And on Wednesday, he did the same as Monday.

Given that the red tank is smaller than the green, which tank now contains the most paint of the other colour?

 Solve this additional puzzle for 5 bonus points:

Which tank is the most removed from its intended shade of paint?

Puzzle
60

CRYPT-OLOGY

Points
10

Mystic Molly's number one ride at the carnival is the Ghost Ride. Along the way, observant riders will notice the famous Cryptic Bats.

Using the clues to help you, can you crack their code and say what the five words are?

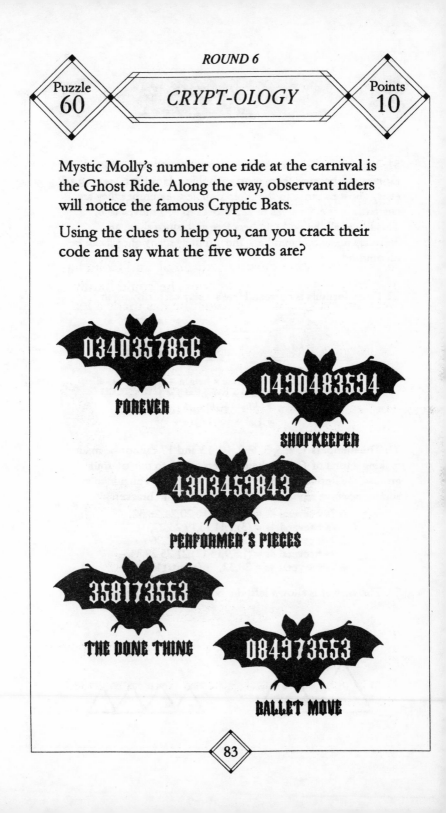

0340357856
FOREVER

0490483594
SHOPKEEPER

4303459843
PERFORMER'S PIECES

358173553
THE DONE THING

084973553
BALLET MOVE

51. You cannot ask the ghost in Room 1 to move to room infinity + 1 because there is no such thing. However, you can ask every ghost to move to the room double the number they are currently in (i.e. 1 moves to 2, 2 moves to 4, 3 moves to 6, etc.) This leaves all the odd numbers free and, since there are infinitely many odd numbers, the infinitely many ghosts can be accommodated.

52. Eric's formula is correct. Here's a way of justifying it:

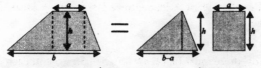

Area of triangle $= \frac{1}{2} \times$ base $\times$ height $= \frac{1}{2} \times (b-a) \times h$
Area of rectangle $=$ base $\times$ height $= a \times h$
Total area $= [\frac{1}{2}bh - \frac{1}{2}ah] + ah$
$= \frac{1}{2}ah + \frac{1}{2}bh = \frac{1}{2}(a+b)h$

53. The numbers 1, 2, 3, 5, 6, 9, 10, 13 and 17 cannot be made, making a total of 66. All the numbers fall in to one of four groups; the impossible combinations are those which involve adding negative amounts of 4s (shown here in brackets):

$$0 \text{ 7s} + \text{several 4s} = 0,4,8,12,16,20,24,28,32,\cdots$$
$$1 \text{ 7s} + \text{several 4s} = (3),7,11,15,19,23,27,\cdots$$
$$2 \text{ 7s} + \text{several 4s} = (2,6,10),14,18,22,26,\cdots$$
$$3 \text{ 7s} + \text{several 4s} = (1,5,9,13,17),21,25,29,33,\cdots$$
$$4 \text{ 7s} + \text{several 4s} = 28,32,\cdots \text{ (as first line)}.$$

54. The answer is shown left; the bonus answer is on the right:

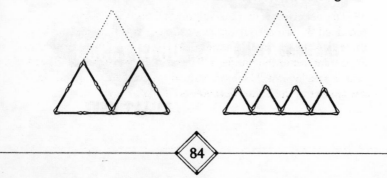

55. The answer is CON. You can't spell CONVENT because it is not possible to lift the letter V without disturbing the E.

56. Both statements are correct because the other object isn't man-made. It is the Great Barrier Reef, which is a coral made from thousands of sea animals.

57. A picture of a stork would be suitable. All the other pictures pair up in rows with one letter different. Row 1 = Stork + Storm; Row 2 = Plant + Plane; Row 3 = Steam + Steak; Row 4 = Chess + Chest.

58. Clearly, there must be $(21+9+6)/3 = 12$ eggs in each basket. There are only three possible starting moves: (a) double the 6 basket moving 6 from the 9 basket; (b) double the 6 basket by moving 6 from the 21 basket; or (c) double the 9 basket by moving 9 from the 21 basket. It turns out that (b) provides the right answer, and (a) (not illustrated) or (c) (shown below on the right) provides an answer for the bonus puzzle.

	Main Answer			Bonus Answer		
Move 1	21	9	6	21	9	6
	15	9	12	12	18	6
Move 2	15	9	12	12	18	6
	6	18	12	12	12	12
Move 3	6	18	12			
	12	12	12			

59. The net effect is that the volumes of both tanks have remained the same, so if red paint has got into the green tank, there must be the same amount of green paint in the red tank. So the answer to the puzzle is "Neither". However, since the red tank is smaller, it will be more contaminated than the green, so the answer to the bonus question is "The red tank".

60. If you managed to guess the clues and match them up to the numbers, you may have seen that the letters used correspond to the top row of a typewriter keyboard:

1	2	3	4	5	6	7	8	9	0
Q	W	E	R	T	Y	U	I	O	P

So the answers are: 0340357856 = PERPETUITY; 0490483594 = PROPRIETOR; 4303459843 = REPERTOIRE; 358173553 = ETIQUETTE; 084973553 = PIROUETTE.

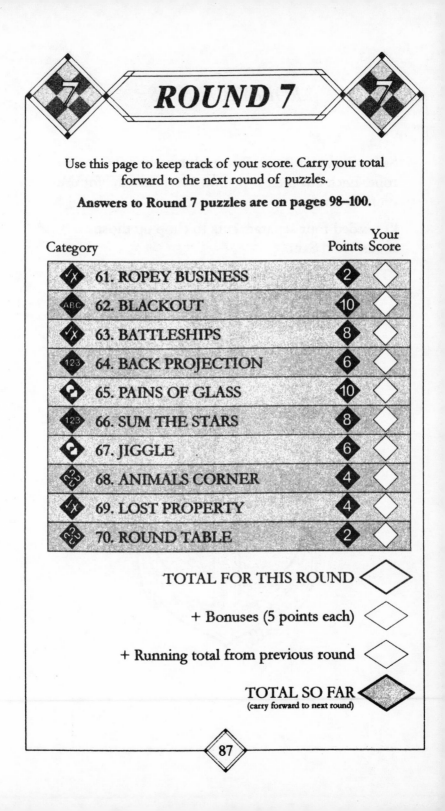

ROUND 7

Use this page to keep track of your score. Carry your total forward to the next round of puzzles.

Answers to Round 7 puzzles are on pages 98–100.

Category	Points	Your Score
61. ROPEY BUSINESS	2	◇
62. BLACKOUT	10	◇
63. BATTLESHIPS	8	◇
64. BACK PROJECTION	6	◇
65. PAINS OF GLASS	10	◇
66. SUM THE STARS	8	◇
67. JIGGLE	6	◇
68. ANIMALS CORNER	4	◇
69. LOST PROPERTY	4	◇
70. ROUND TABLE	2	◇

TOTAL FOR THIS ROUND ◇

+ Bonuses (5 points each) ◇

+ Running total from previous round ◇

TOTAL SO FAR ◆
(carry forward to next round)

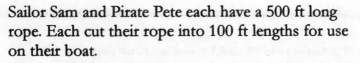

Sailor Sam and Pirate Pete each have a 500 ft long rope. Each cut their rope into 100 ft lengths for use on their boat.

"I needed four separate cuts to chop up those ropes," said Sam.

"That's strange, me hearty, I needed five cuts," said a puzzled Pirate Pete.

Can you explain the difference?

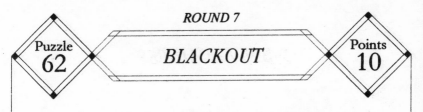

Will the Wordsmith sells crosswords. To advertise his wares, he has just finished painting this crossword in his shop window. From the inside of the shop it looks like this:

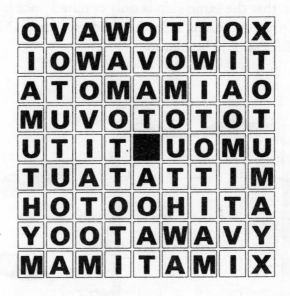

Will is very pleased with it so far. "All I need to do now is paint out 30 more squares to make a proper crossword with half-turn symmetry."

How should he do it?

In the carnival boat pond there are five motorized battleships for the children to play with, numbered from 1 to 5 as shown. The numbers along the edge of the pond denote the total of all those ships appearing in that sector of the pond.

Given that the same ship is only counted once in each row or column, help the children locate where the ships should be placed.

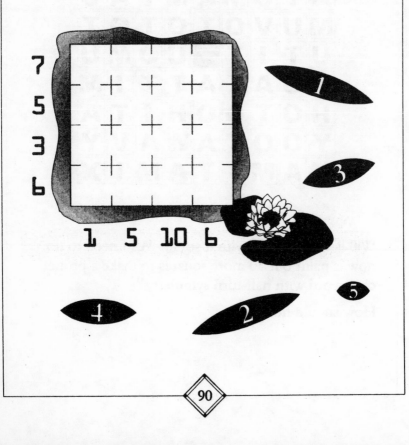

BACK PROJECTION

A model rocket is launched. When the projectile reaches the highest point of its flight (namely, 36 ft) another rocket is launched from the same place.

What will the maximum height of the second rocket be, given that they land on the ground at the same place at the same time?

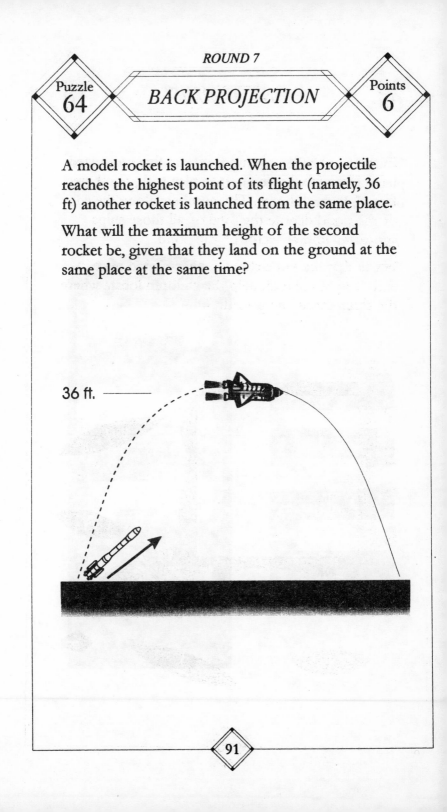

36 ft. ————

Visual Vern challenges you to place the etched glass pieces into the window so that an 8-letter word can be read. It can be done.

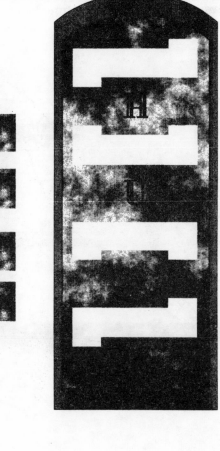

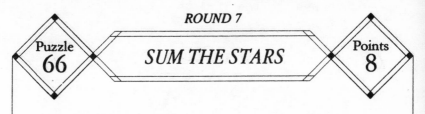

SUM THE STARS

Insert the remaining numbers (i.e. from 4 to 12 inclusive) so that (a) all the pairs of connected circles add up to the same total, and (b) all the stars add up to same number.

N.B. The totals mentioned in (a) and (b) are not the same.

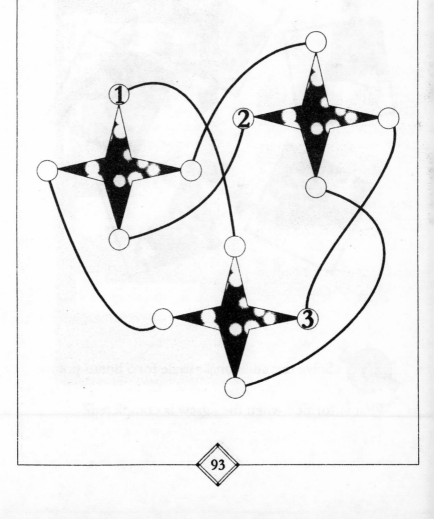

How can these five jigsaw pieces be fitted together?

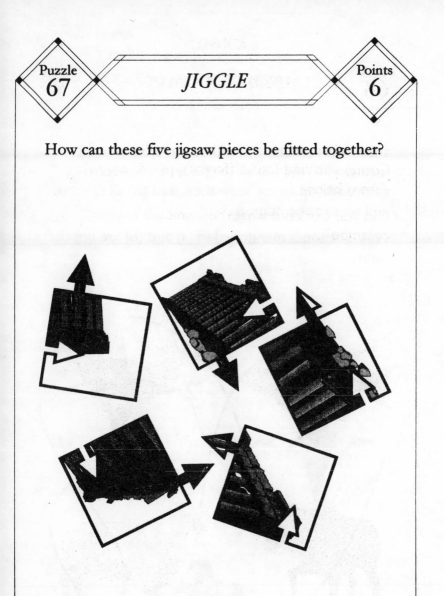

Solve this additional puzzle for 5 bonus points:

What is formed when the jigsaw is completed?

ANIMALS CORNER

On a subsequent visit to the carnival's Animals Corner you find four different types of animal, shown below.

Can you work out what these animals have in common?

"My job's not an easy one," grumbles Guy the Security Guard. "People lose all sorts of things while they're on the carnival's rides – binoculars, umbrellas, hats, belts, cameras, and so on.

"All the lost property gets sent to my hut and, in order to keep things organized, I arrange the things logically on my shelves. And if you want a puzzle to work out, tell me where I should place a shoe in order to keep my system going."

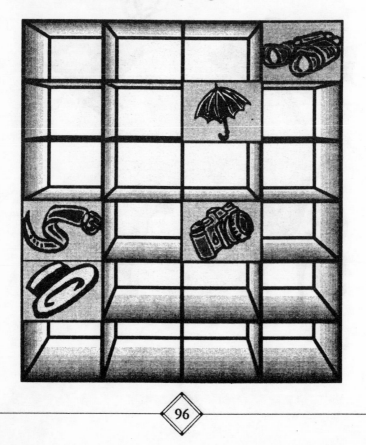

Visual Vern is proudly displaying his new circular
pool table. "I never was any good at corner shots!"
he jokes. If he were to hit the ball so that it hits the
table four-ninths of the way around the
circumference, how many times would the ball
need to bounce to return to its starting position?

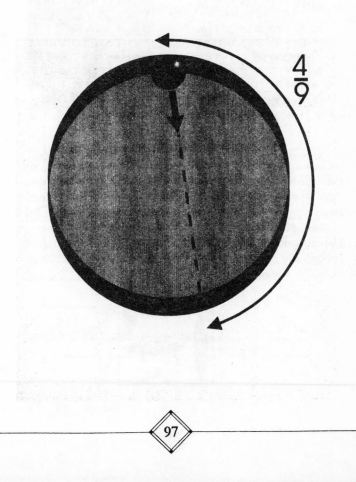

61. Sailor Sam had a straight piece of rope which was 500 ft long. Pirate Pete started with a circular rope of that length and so needed one more cut to reach the same situation as Sam.

62. This is a tricky puzzle that becomes much easier when you realize that Will meant people to see the crossword from outside the shop. So, you need to consider the puzzle back-to-front, shown left. The answer (shown right) demonstrates which squares should be blanked out.

63. This can be deduced logically. Boat 1 must be in the first column and, as it is 3 squares long, it must occupy the middle two squares. This means that boat 2 must fit in the remaining three squares in the third row. The third column must contain boats 3 and 5, and the bottom row must contain boats 1 and 5 (it cannot be 2 & 4 as we have now placed boat 2 elsewhere). Hence, boat 5 must appear at the intersection of the third column and the bottom row. From there it is not difficult to deduce the answer:

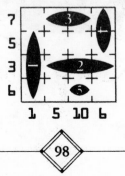

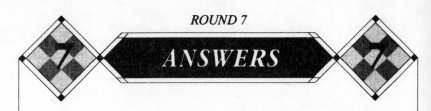

ANSWERS

64. The time of flight for a projectile is proportional to the square of the maximum height. In plain English, halving the time of flight would reduce the maximum height by ½ squared, i.e. ¼. So the maximum height of the second rocket would be 36/4 = 9 feet.

65. The secret is to realize you can rotate or flip over the tiles by using the symmetry of the letters:

66. Each pair of numbers must add up to 13, hence every star must have numbers totalling 26. Here is one solution:

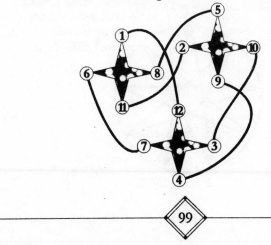

67. The pieces lock together in a cyclical formation to form a picture of the Acropolis in Athens, Greece:

68. Their names are the same in the singular or plural. For example, you can have one sheep or several sheep. (The plural of fish can be "fish" or "fishes".)

69. As SHOE has two consonants, it should be on the second row of shelves from the bottom and, as it has two vowels, it should be in the second column. The other objects follow this logic also.

70. The ball would need to bounce nine times (eight if you don't count the final bounce). This happens because 4 and 9 do not share any common factors (except 1).

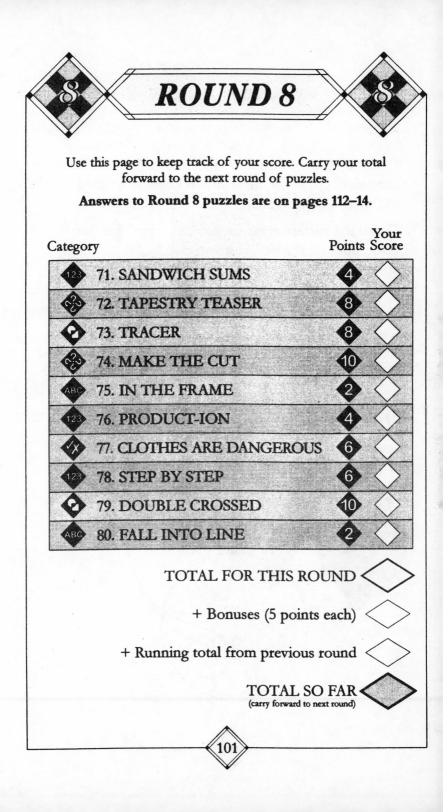

ROUND 8

Use this page to keep track of your score. Carry your total forward to the next round of puzzles.

Answers to Round 8 puzzles are on pages 112–14.

Category	Points	Your Score
71. SANDWICH SUMS	4	◇
72. TAPESTRY TEASER	8	◇
73. TRACER	8	◇
74. MAKE THE CUT	10	◇
75. IN THE FRAME	2	◇
76. PRODUCT-ION	4	◇
77. CLOTHES ARE DANGEROUS	6	◇
78. STEP BY STEP	6	◇
79. DOUBLE CROSSED	10	◇
80. FALL INTO LINE	2	◇

TOTAL FOR THIS ROUND ◇

+ Bonuses (5 points each) ◇

+ Running total from previous round ◇

TOTAL SO FAR ◇
(carry forward to next round)

Colin the Clown wants to make himself a sandwich. However, he wants to know how large the slices of bread are.

Given the surface areas (in square inches) for the three sides of the loaf, can you give Colin the answer?

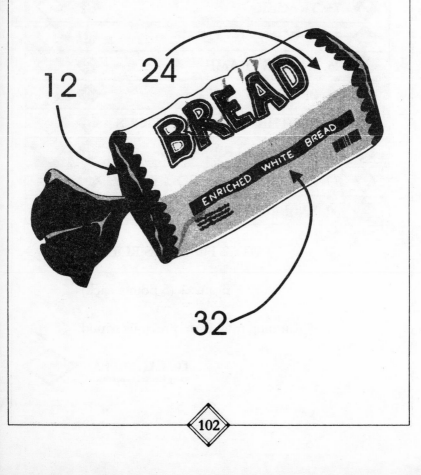

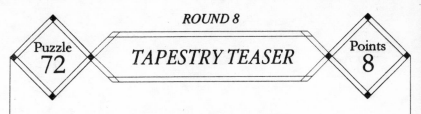

TAPESTRY TEASER

Mystic Molly is weaving a tapestry. The diagrams show she has built it up in a sequence. Can you supply the next picture?

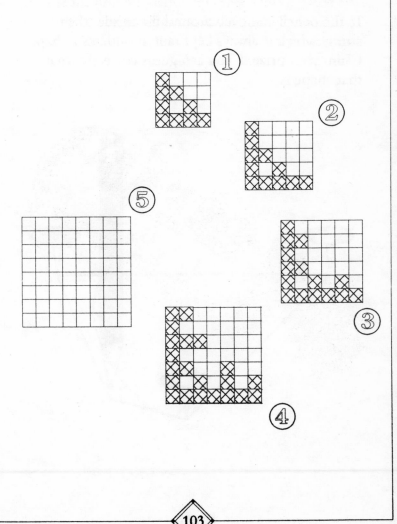

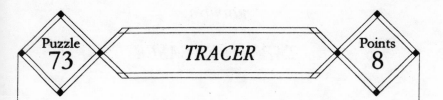

Visual Vern offers visitors to his stall a wide variety
of visual puzzles. For this particular game he has
three tacks hammered into a piece of board with a
string around them.

If the pencil is moved around the inside of the
string, which is always kept taut, it outlines a shape.
Claim your prize if you can guess correctly what
that shape is.

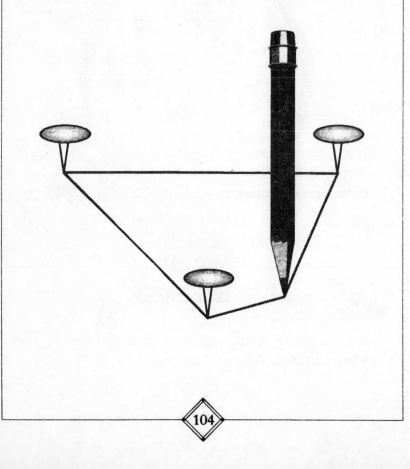

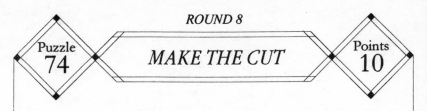

MAKE THE CUT

Here is an 8 ft long piece of string which needs to be cut up into two 1 ft and three 2 ft lengths.

What is the least number of cuts you would need to achieve this feat?

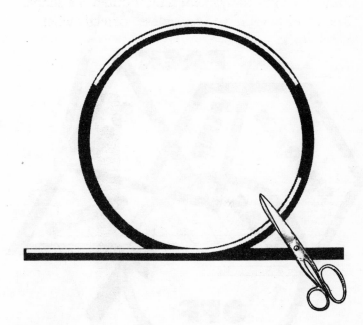

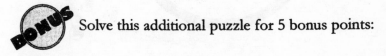 Solve this additional puzzle for 5 bonus points:

How many cuts would you need for a 10 ft string to be cut into 1, 2, 3 and 4 ft lengths?

Can you think of a word that would logically fit into the arrowed space?

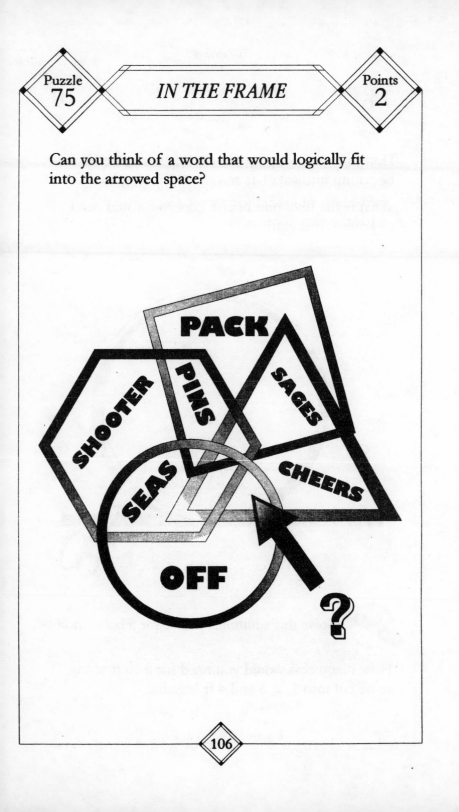

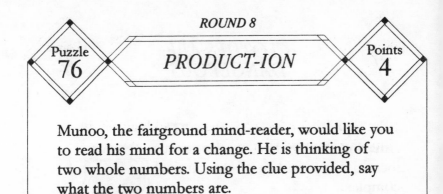

Puzzle
76

PRODUCT-ION

Points
4

Munoo, the fairground mind-reader, would like you to read his mind for a change. He is thinking of two whole numbers. Using the clue provided, say what the two numbers are.

Their product is three times larger than their sum.

Jane appears as an assistant to "The Amazing Stupendo" at the circus located in the middle of the carnival complex.

On her day off, she decided that she would have a change of scene so she went to the nearest town to buy herself some new clothes for the act. She purchased a satin dress, gold bangles, black gloves, silver high-heeled shoes, belt and various other accessories to complete the look.

Just before the act, The Amazing Stupendo was not pleased with his assistant's new ensemble. "You better go and change, if you want to stay alive!"

Why did he say this?

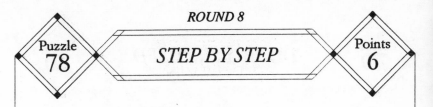

STEP BY STEP

This athlete wears a pedometer, a device used to measure the number of steps taken. Its current reading is:

After running a certain track event, his pedometer reads another palindromic number. Given that his pace is 1 m per stride, what race did he run?

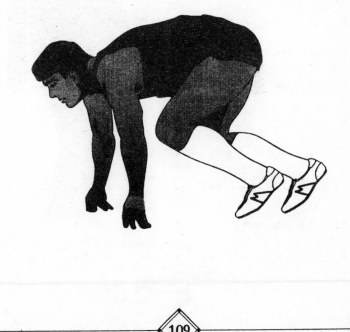

Visual Vern offers you four
identical stone pieces, like the one
shown right.

Rearrange them to form a cross.
Then rearrange them again to
make a cross of the same shape
and size but different shade.

The grid below may help you.

. . . .

. . . .

. . . .

. . . .

. . . .

. . . .

. . . .

. . . .

. . . .

. . . .

FALL INTO LINE

Will the Wordsmith takes some lettered stones out of a bag and places them on a table. He then takes some chalk and draws a dotted line as well as some arrows.

"To win the game, tell me where I went on holiday," he says.

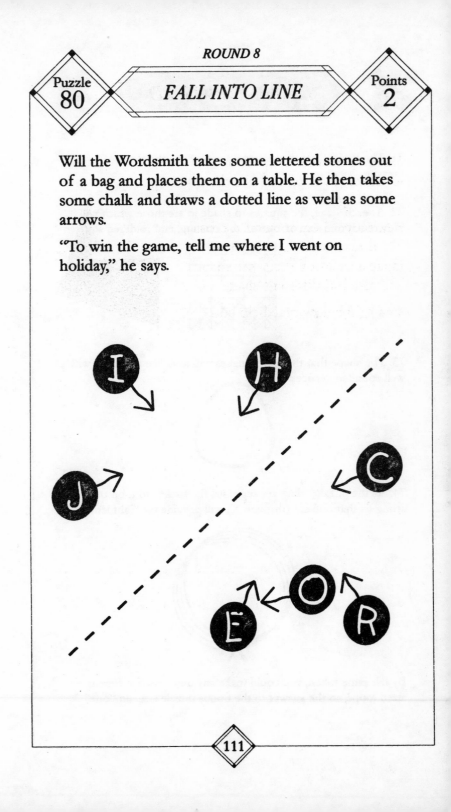

71. The loaf of bread measures $3 \times 4 \times 8$, so the slices of bread measure 3 inches by 4 inches.

72. At each stage, the squares to shade in are those which will only touch one side of one of the existing, embroidered squares.

73. The shape that the pencil makes will look like a triangle with well-rounded vertices:

74. As the puzzle's diagram suggests, the trick is to loop the string so that one cut (through X) will provide the right lengths.

By the same token, you could make any number of different sized loops, so the answer to the bonus puzzle is again "one".

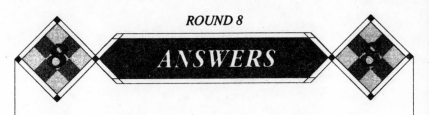

ANSWERS

75. The arrow points to the intersection of the triangle (3 sides) and the circle (1 side) so that answer has to suffix 3 + 1 = 4. Suitable words include ball, eyes, wheeled, legged, poster, seater, dimensions, etc. The other phrases are "Four pack" (because "pack" is in the four-sided square), "Three cheers", "One off", "Six shooter", "Ten pins" (6 + 4), "Seven sages" (4 + 3), "Seven seas" (6 + 1).

76. If you have two unknowns but one equation you can't solve it, right? Wrong, because we can use the information that both the numbers are whole integers. If our two numbers are x and y, then "Their product is three times larger than their sum" turns into:

$$xy = 3(x + y) = 3x + 3y$$

So:
$$xy - 3y = 3x$$
$$y(x - 3) = 3x$$
$$y = \frac{3x}{x - 3}$$

As y must be a whole number, $x - 3$ must equal 1, hence $x = 4$ and (using the above equation) it follows that y is 12.

77. "The Amazing Stupendo" is a knife-throwing act. Lucy had bought higher-heeled shoes than she normally buys. If she had worn them for the act, it could have been a dangerous situation.

78. The man must have run the 110 m hurdles race. The only possible palindromes that would be suitable are:

$$73037$$
$$- \underline{72927}$$
$$110$$

79. The two crosses are shown here:

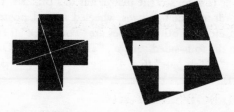

80. The stall holder had been to JERICHO. To see why, move each stone roundel in the direction of the arrows until it meets the dotted line.

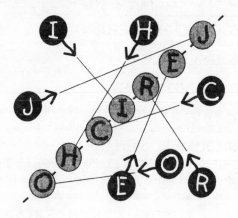

ROUND 9

Use this page to keep track of your score. Carry your total forward to the next round of puzzles.

Answers to Round 9 puzzles are on pages 126–8.

Category	Points	Your Score
81. BOB'S SLEIGH	8	◇
82. STALL TO STALL	10	◇
83. CHAMPION SHIPS	6	◇
84. SIX-SIDED SECTIONS	10	◇
85. CLOCK WATCHING	6	◇
86. ENCIRCLE	2	◇
87. MIXED DATES	4	◇
88. QUITE QUIET	2	◇
89. CRIMEWATCH	8	◇
90. TRIANGLE WRANGLE	4	◇

TOTAL FOR THIS ROUND ◇

+ Bonuses (5 points each) ◇

+ Running total from previous round ◇

TOTAL SO FAR ◇
(carry forward to next round)

BOB'S SLEIGH

Carnival Bob is installing a new bobsleigh ride. He has been given a cryptic map of the route needed. The numbers denote how many half-pipe segments are contained in that row or column for that quadrant. Two pieces have been placed for you – now complete the route.

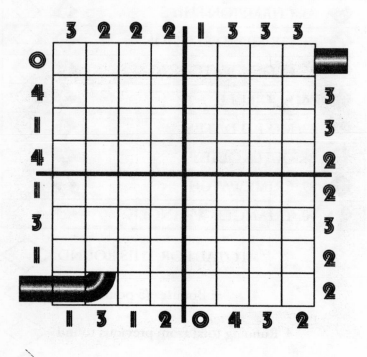

STALL TO STALL

The owner of the carnival wishes to make an ideal route plan for his visitors. He wants them to be able to (a) visit every square (except the carnival offices), and (b) visit a stall at every fifth square. The entrance and exits are denoted in the diagram below.

How should the owner plot the route?

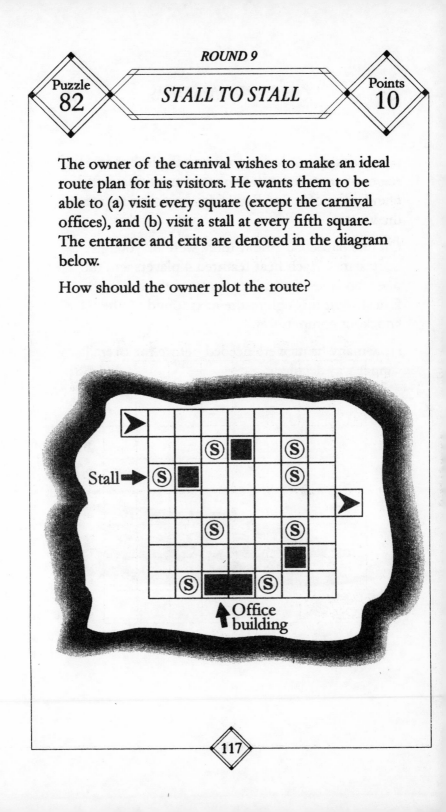

Stall →

Office building

Every Friday on the carnival boating lake there is a remote-controlled motor boat competition, with a grand prize of a free day of fairground rides for the winner.

On one particular Friday there were 82 young contestants. Each heat featured 4 players and the one who steered their boat around the buoys the fastest went through to the next round of the knockout competition.

How many heats were needed before the overall winner was decided?

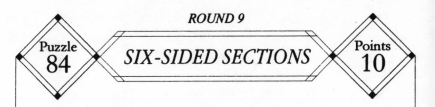

SIX-SIDED SECTIONS

Marvin the Magician has two pieces of hexagonal plastic which he uses for a special card trick in his act. However, at the moment he's using them for some "trick-y" mathematics.

"Here is a yellow hexagon overlapping with a magenta one. They are regular hexagons each with an area of 30 square inches. As you might expect, the overlap is green. To win the game you must tell me the area of the green section."

Hint: A straight edge may be useful in this puzzle.

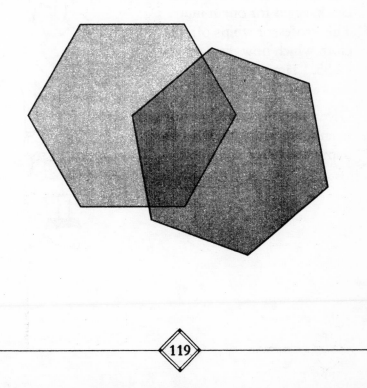

"I have invented a time machine that can make time go forwards, backwards or stand still!" Professor Muddleup proudly proclaims. He points towards an old digital clock currently showing the time 12:55.

He then takes a cloth and covers the clock for one minute. Upon taking off the cloth, the clock shows 12:56. "No surprises, yet. But watch this ..." He covers the clock again, this time for two minutes. This time the clock says 12:56 when uncovered. "Time has stood still!", exclaims the Professor.

For the finale, he covers the clock, again for one minute. The Professor whips off the cloth which now displays 12:55. "Time has gone backwards!" he screams.

Given that the clock has not been tampered with, what has happened here?

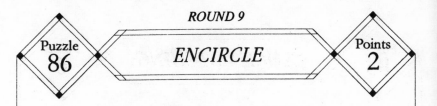

ENCIRCLE

A street-show performer wishes to entertain the carnival's visitors. She is a juggling act and so wishes to have as much room as possible, although she has a limited 100 foot chain to help her cordon off the space she needs.

In what configuration should she arrange the cordon to achieve this? She can use the walls available to help her in this feat.

Penny, a secretary to the carnival owner, is making plans for the next few holiday seasons. She uses the well-known rule that Christmas Day and New Year's Day always fall on the same day of the week.

However, she is surprised to hear that in the year 2000 Christmas Day will fall on Monday whereas New Year's Day falls on a Saturday.

Can you explain why her rule doesn't work?

To win this game, find the 9-letter word that is spelled out using one silent letter from each of the words below. The first word gives you the first letter, and so on.

HAUTBOY

AISLE

TABLEAUX

BUSINESS

HANDSOME

TWITCHED

FORECASTLE

MNEMONIC

PRAYER

One of the fairground security guards hands you a
piece of paper. "Dunno what this means," he says,
"but I reckon this is the work of the infamous
bank robber Lex Lucra."

Can you work out what the message reads?

TRIANGLE WRANGLE

How can these six identical rods be arranged to make a total of eight equilateral triangles? Six of the triangles are the same size, and the other two are also congruent to one another.

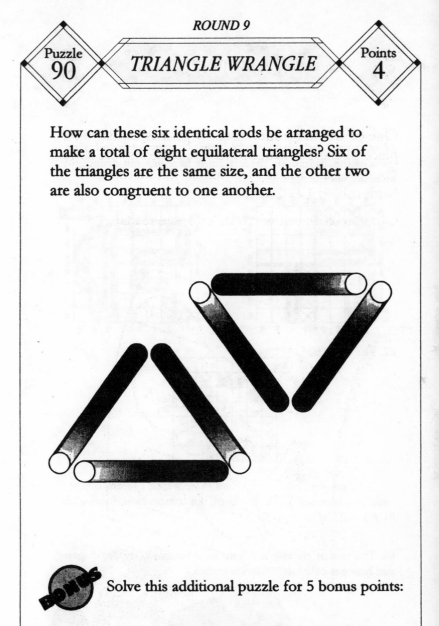

Solve this additional puzzle for 5 bonus points:

How can the same six rods make four equilateral triangles so that they all exist in different planes in space?

81. Clearly the rows and columns with "0" cannot have any part of the route, and those with "4" must be completely full. This gives us the diagram on the left. From here one can deduce the solution, shown right.

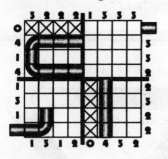 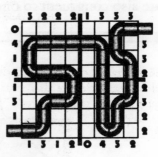

82. The route is:

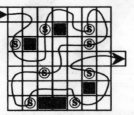

83. If 82 contestants entered then there were 81 losers. Since each heat knocked 3 people out of the competition, there were 81 / 3 = 27 heats.

84. The area of overlap is 2/6ths of a hexagon (see the diagram) and hence is equal to 10 square inches.

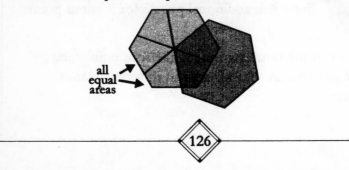

all equal areas

ANSWERS

85. Although the clock has not been tampered with, it is rather old. One of the lights has broken which explains why the times were not as expected.

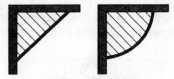

This LED is broken

86. A straight cordon would yield an area of 250 square yards. However, circles are always the best for maximizing area. A quarter circle yields an area of 318 square yards.

87. When people say "Christmas Day and New Year's Day fall on the same day of the week", they really mean "New Year's Day is seven days after Christmas Day". However, that New Year's Day lies in the next year. There is nothing special about the year 2000 – January 1st and December 25th of the same year are always one day apart (two days apart during leap years, like the year 2000).

88. Taking one of the silent letters from each word spells out TAXIDERMY:

HAU(T)BOY
(A)ISLE
TABLEAU(X)
BUS(I)NESS
HAN(D)SOME
TWITCH(E)D
FO(R)ECASTLE
(M)NEMONIC
PRA(Y)ER

89. If you arrange the shapes by their number of sides you should be able to work out the message "PUT THE MONEY OUT OF FRONT WINDOW NOW – L."

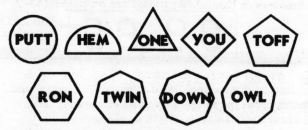

90. Moving one of the large triangles over the other produces the required result, which looks like a Star of David:

To answer the bonus question, we clearly need the use of the third dimension. This pyramid satisfies the required condition:

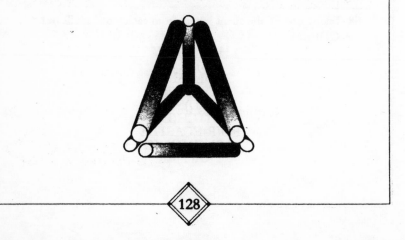

ROUND 10

Use this page to keep track of your score. Carry your total forward to the next round of puzzles.

Answers to Round 10 puzzles are on pages 140–2.

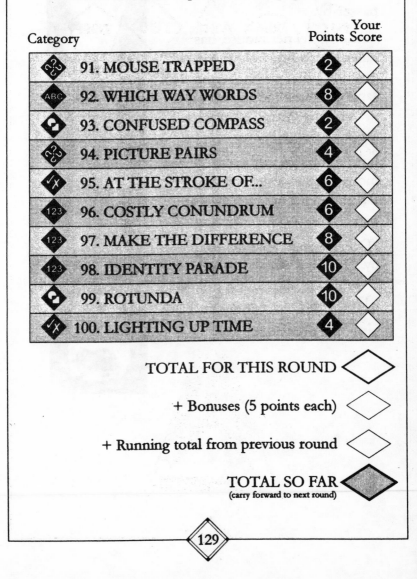

Category	Points	Your Score
91. MOUSE TRAPPED	2	◇
92. WHICH WAY WORDS	8	◇
93. CONFUSED COMPASS	2	◇
94. PICTURE PAIRS	4	◇
95. AT THE STROKE OF...	6	◇
96. COSTLY CONUNDRUM	6	◇
97. MAKE THE DIFFERENCE	8	◇
98. IDENTITY PARADE	10	◇
99. ROTUNDA	10	◇
100. LIGHTING UP TIME	4	◇

TOTAL FOR THIS ROUND ◇

+ Bonuses (5 points each) ◇

+ Running total from previous round ◇

TOTAL SO FAR ◆
(carry forward to next round)

One of the younger visitors to the fairground was crying. "What's the matter?" asked a passer-by.

"Timmy, my pet mouse, has fallen down that hole in the ground. I was playing in the sand pit when Timmy fell into it," said the distressed child.

The passer-by looked down the hole and could just make out the mouse at the bottom. It had fallen down a hole left by a tent peg.

"Don't worry," said the passer-by. "I have a way we can get Timmy out, although it will take a little time."

How did they do it?

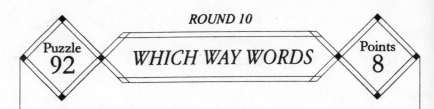

WHICH WAY WORDS

Wordsmith Will has got himself into a bit of a mess. Using the coordinate grid shown on the left, he had encoded the large crossword. Unfortunately, he has written the numbers in a haphazard fashion so that, for example, if a square contains 2 & 3 he can't decide whether he meant row 2 column 3 (the "S") or row 3 column 2 (the "O").

Nevertheless, can you work out what the four 5-letter words are?

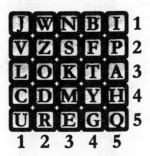

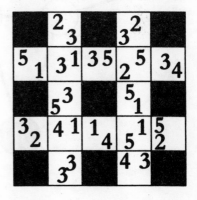

If a move consists of rolling a ball along a line into an empty space, how many moves will it take for this compass to be made correct (with North pointing to the top of the page)?

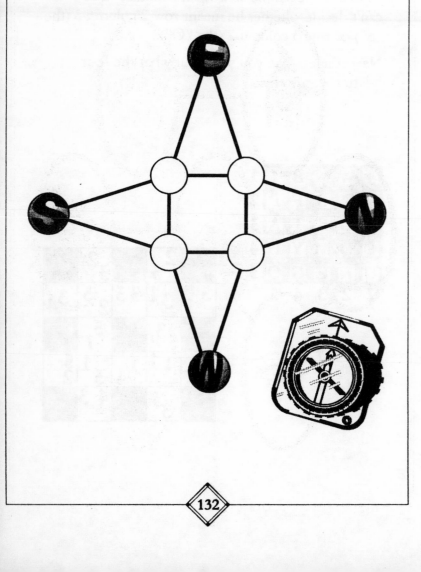

PICTURE PAIRS

The following seven pictures hang in the Picture Palace. They match up in adjacent pairs to make phrases. Which is the red herring?

Mandy Math has a new puzzle waiting for you at the Number Cruncher stall. "Here's a fountain pen. Using the least number of strokes of the pen, how is it possible to make the mathematical sum on this piece of paper correct?"

$$1 + 2 - 3 = 139$$

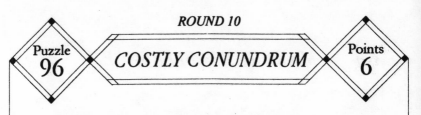

COSTLY CONUNDRUM

Colin the Clown is on balloon duty today. Visitors to the carnival are invited to buy one of his novelty balloons for a very reasonable price.

There are six shapes of balloon, each one costing a different amount (namely 1, 2, 3, 5, 7 and 10 pence).

Jamie's mother wishes to buy some for her son and his friends. Unfortunately she has forgotten which shapes were required. However she does know that she needs four each of three of the shapes, and five each for the other three shapes.

Given that she was able to buy what she needed using only 20 pence coins, what balloons were bought?

MAKE THE DIFFERENCE

"Look at these triangles," says Mandy Math.

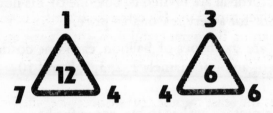

"The number inside each triangle is calculated by taking the (positive) difference between each pair of numbers. To take the first one as an example:

$$12 = (7 - 1) + (4 - 1) + (7 - 4).$$

Can you tell me:

(a) Under what circumstances will the number inside the triangle be a multiple of 4?

(b) Under what circumstances will the number inside the triangle be even, but NOT a multiple of 4?"

Solve this additional puzzle for 5 bonus points:

Under what circumstances will the number inside the triangle be odd?

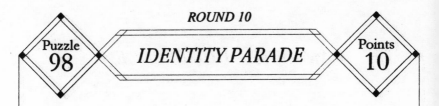

Inspector Hartland is lining up eight suspects in an identity parade. Unfortunately, they have got themselves mixed up. He can ask any suspect to come out of the parade and move into any gap in the line-up (asking the others to shuffle up if necessary).

What is the least number of suspects he will have to ask to move so that they line up in numerical order from left to right?

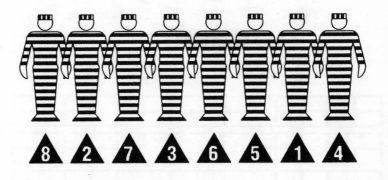

How can the three strips of paper be wound around the three middle rows of the cylinder so that the three shaded segments at either end are joined together by a line? Continue straight on at crossroads.

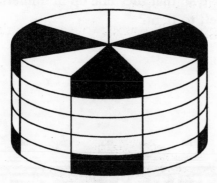

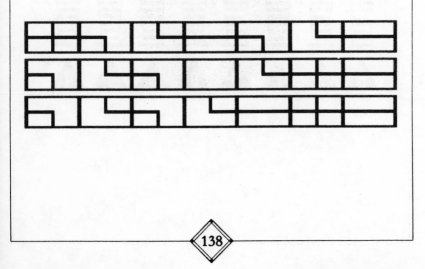

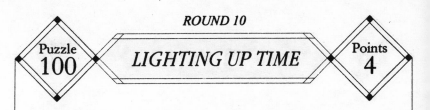

LIGHTING UP TIME

Lateral Larry has brought out his "lamp in a box" puzzle again. "Here are two switches, of which neither, one or both could control the lightbulb in the closed, black box. I can tell you that the bulb is currently off.

"You are only allowed to open the box once, and once you do so you must tell me which switch(es), if either, control the lamp."

What strategy should you use to win every time?

91. By taking some sand from the sandpit, the passer-by could fill up the hole gradually. Hopefully the mouse would shuffle its feet to keep on top of the sand.

92.

93. It will require a total of ten moves:

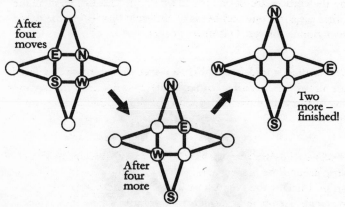

94. The eye is the odd one out. The other pictures pair up to make the phrases "witch doctor", "Roman candle" and "finger painting".

95. Just one stroke of the pen is necessary:

$$14^2 - 3 = 139$$

96. She buys four of each shape of balloon plus one extra for three of the types. The four of each shape would cost a total of $(1 + 2 + 3 + 5 + 7 + 10) \times 4 = £1.12$.

Since we know the total amount was a multiple of 20p, possible totals for all the balloons include £1.20, £1.40, £1.60, £1.80, and so on. This means the extra three balloons must have cost a total of 8p, 28p, 48p, 68p, and so on. Using three of the values 1, 2, 3, 5, 7 and 10, the only possible total is 8p. Hence the mother spent £1.20. Therefore, she bought four 3, 7 and 10 pence balloons and five 1, 2 and 5 pence balloons.

97. (a) The number inside the triangle occurs when the numbers on the vertices are all odd (or all even). (b) This occurs in all the other cases, i.e. one number is of different "parity" to the other two. Bonus answer: This never occurs.

98. Reading from left to right, we notice that suspects 2, 3 and 4 are already in the correct order. So we only need to ask the other five suspects to move in order for them to read in order from 1 to 8.

99. The strips are given in the correct order, so wrap the first strip around the first ring and likewise for the second and third strips. Imagine the cylinder has been flattened out into a rectangle. Arrow indicates where the start of the strip begins.

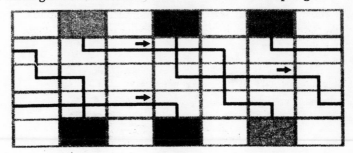

100. You can use the same rule as before (that is, use the two physical principles of light and heat). However, the logic you need to use is different. Turn on switch 1 for 10 minutes, then turn off. Turn on switch 2 and immediately open the box. Then you can reason as follows:

	LAMP ON?	
	YES	NO
LAMP HOT? YES	Switch 1 & 2 turn lamp on	Switch 1 turns lamp on
NO	Switch 2 turns lamp on	No switch turns lamp on

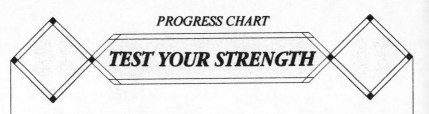

TEST YOUR STRENGTH

How are you doing? Calculate your score so far and
see how high you can try...

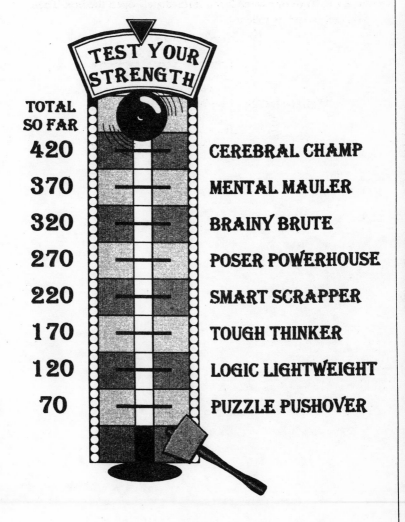

TOTAL SO FAR

420	**CEREBRAL CHAMP**
370	**MENTAL MAULER**
320	**BRAINY BRUTE**
270	**POSER POWERHOUSE**
220	**SMART SCRAPPER**
170	**TOUGH THINKER**
120	**LOGIC LIGHTWEIGHT**
70	**PUZZLE PUSHOVER**

ROUND 11

Use this page to keep track of your score. Carry your total forward to the next round of puzzles.

Answers to Round 11 puzzles are on pages 156–8.

Category	Points	Your Score
101. WORD WEB	8	◇
102. PICK A POCKET	2	◇
103. CIRCULATION	4	◇
104. CYGNET CIPHER	8	◇
105. TRACKING	4	◇
106. IN PIECES?	6	◇
107. SERIAL SERIES	6	◇
108. ALL SQUARE	10	◇
109. STEP ON UP	2	◇
110. THREE IN A ROW	10	◇

TOTAL FOR THIS ROUND ◇

+ Bonuses (5 points each) ◇

+ Running total from previous round ◇

TOTAL SO FAR ◇
(carry forward to next round)

Using all the perspex roundels illustrated, arrange
the letters so that **ANY** downward route from start
to finish will spell out a 4-letter word.

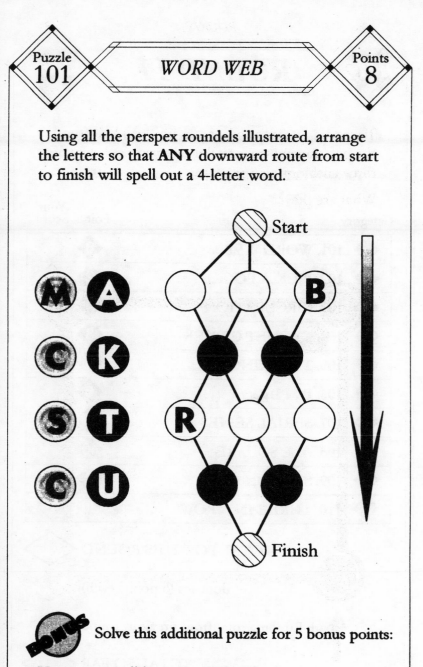

Solve this additional puzzle for 5 bonus points:

How many valid routes are there?

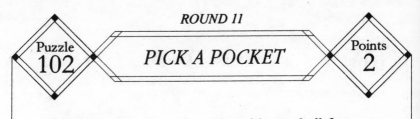

PICK A POCKET

There are two ways of potting this cue ball from the position shown into the arrowed pocket using three cushions along the way.

What are they?

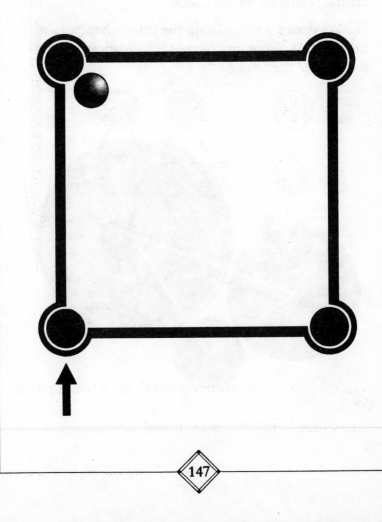

Mandy Math takes out three over-sized coins. "You should have seen the vending machine these came from," she quips. The largest coin is three times wider than the smallest; the medium coin is twice as large as the smallest. The smallest coin is two inches in diameter. She draws lines between the central points of all the coins.

"I have drawn a line joining the three midpoints of the coins. Without any further information, tell me the area of the triangle."

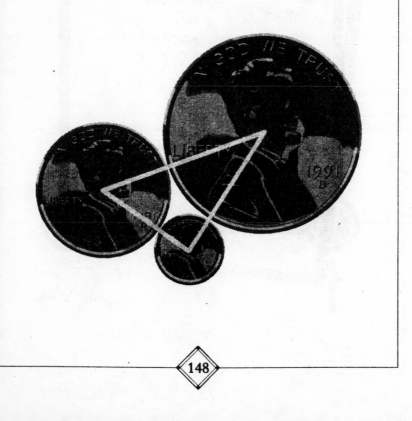

CYGNET CYPHER

In the Animals Corner of the carnival, you see a sign besides an enclosure where some of the young chicks are kept. Can you work out the message?

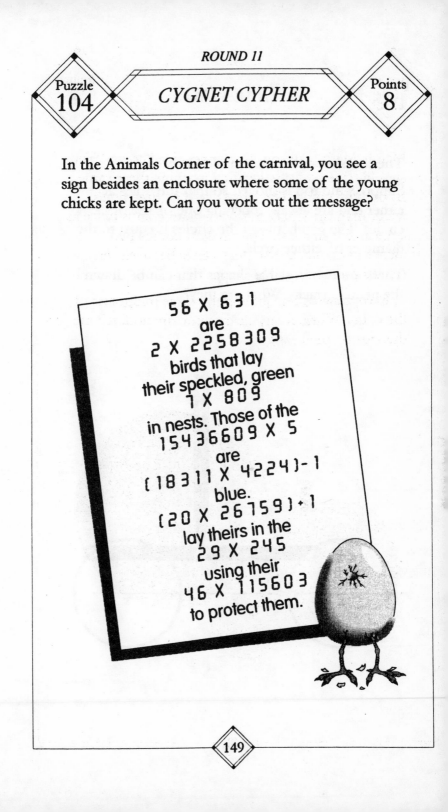

56 X 631

are

2 X 2258309

birds that lay

their speckled, green

7 X 809

in nests. Those of the

15436609 X 5

are

(18311 X 4224)-1

blue.

(20 X 26759)+1

lay theirs in the

29 X 245

using their

46 X 115603

to protect them.

The rod shown has three holes in it.

Suppose the rod is moved so that the holes at either end are always touching one of the black circles. The gap between the circles is equal to the diameter of either circle.

There are two possible shapes that can be drawn by the pencil's tracks. What are they?

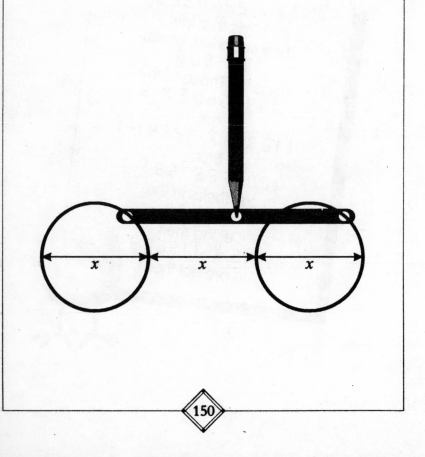

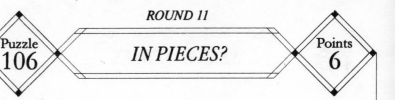

IN PIECES?

Lateral Larry was trying to trick passers-by with an extravagant claim.

"Last year I went on a certain journey.

"At the end of my travels, I discovered that my knees had gone 3 yards further than my feet, my torso had gone 3 yards further than my knees, and my head had gone 3 yards further than my torso."

Given that his journey was a long haul, can you see how Larry can justify his claim?

SERIAL SERIES

This sequence of numbers was calculated using a well-known series and the subtraction operation. Can you work out what the originating series is?

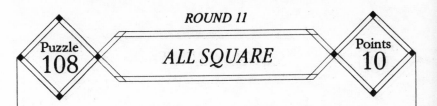

At the moment, the lines painted on these cogs form a square. The larger cogs have 36 teeth and the smaller ones have 15.

How many times does the arrowed cog turn clockwise before the next time a square is formed?

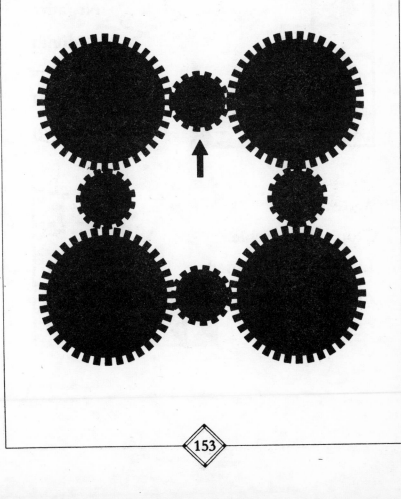

Fill in the staircases using the clues provided. The phrase "MY ARRANGEMENTS GLUE ON" will help you in both cases.

Negative

Month

Teeth holders

Royal

Bank note (slang)

Activated

Tropical vegetable

Looking self-satisfied

Alcoholic drink

Cheese maker?

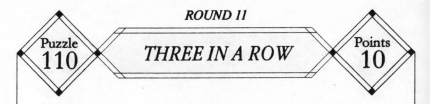

"Here's one that's a bit different," challenges Mandy Math, holding a blackboard showing six circles (see below). "There are many ways in which you can draw a straight line through exactly three circles. Adding these three numbers gives a total. The line given as an example totals 22."

How many different totals are possible in this way?

101. Placing the roundels on similarly shaded spaces, we get:

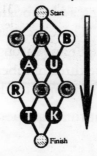

There are 12 words that can be formed (cart, cast, cask, mart, mast, mask, must, muck, musk, bust, busk, buck).

102.

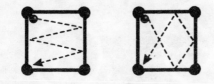

103. It can be seen from the diagram that the triangle has sides of 3, 4 and 5 inches. This triangle is well-known for being right-angled because it is a Pythagorean triplet (because $3^2+4^2=5^2$). Hence the area is $\frac{1}{2} \times$ base $\times$ height = 6 square inches.

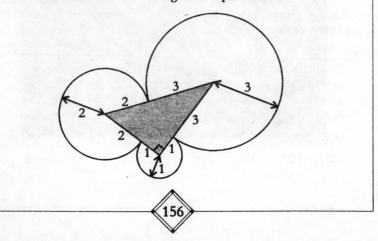

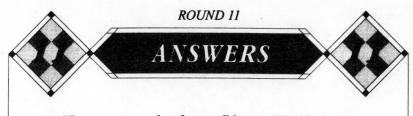

104. The sums are used to form well-known "Upside-down calculator" words. As an example, $56 \times 631 = 35,336$ which looks like this on a calculator when upside-down:

Continuing this for the other sums, the following message is formed:

9EESE are 8199ISh birds that lay their speckled, green E99S in nests. Those of the ShOEBILL are E99ShELL blue. IBISES lay theirs in the SOIL using their BELLIES to protect them.

105. It's pretty obvious that a central circle can be traced. But the other shape is an infinity sign:

106. He had been on a round-the-world trip. This meant that his feet had journeyed around the Earth with radius R, say. His torso was on a circle of radius R + 3 feet, and his head on a circle with radius R + 6 feet. This explains the extra distances.

107. The series is formed from the differences of consecutive pairs of prime numbers. The best clue is that the first number is the only odd number because 2 is the only even number and all successive differences are between odd numbers.

Prime nos.	2		3		5		7		11		13		17		19		23...
Sequence		1		2		2		4		2		4		2		4...	

108. After three turns (not twelve). After moving all the cogs through 45 teeth, the situation is as below. Notice that the lines are in a different orientation now. If the lines had to be in exactly the same position as well, then the answer would have been twelve.

109. This puzzle is a lot easier if you realize the two pyramids have something in common. The letters in the phrase "My arrangements glue on" make up the words in either pyramid.

110. Six totals can be formed:

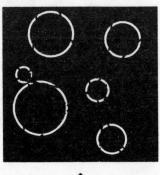

ROUND 12

Use this page to keep track of your score. Carry your total forward to the next round of puzzles.

Answers to Round 12 puzzles are on pages 170–2.

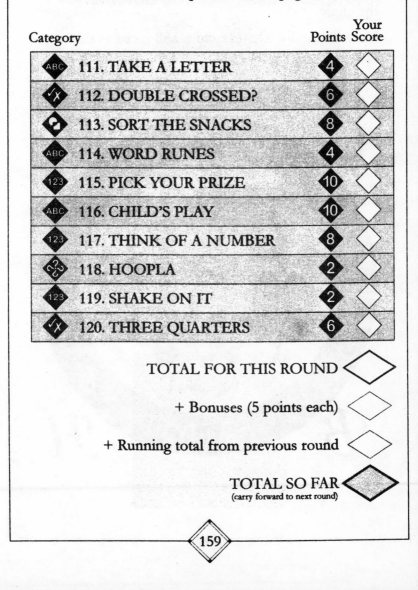

Category	Points	Your Score
ABC 111. TAKE A LETTER	4	◇
√x 112. DOUBLE CROSSED?	6	◇
? 113. SORT THE SNACKS	8	◇
ABC 114. WORD RUNES	4	◇
123 115. PICK YOUR PRIZE	10	◇
ABC 116. CHILD'S PLAY	10	◇
123 117. THINK OF A NUMBER	8	◇
118. HOOPLA	2	◇
123 119. SHAKE ON IT	2	◇
√x 120. THREE QUARTERS	6	◇

TOTAL FOR THIS ROUND ◇

+ Bonuses (5 points each) ◇

+ Running total from previous round ◇

TOTAL SO FAR ◆
(carry forward to next round)

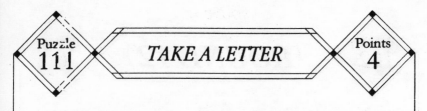

Take a letter from the outside. Then add it on to either end of a 5-letter word, using a clue from the ring. This should give you one of the objects inside the circle.

How do the four letters, clues and pictures match up?

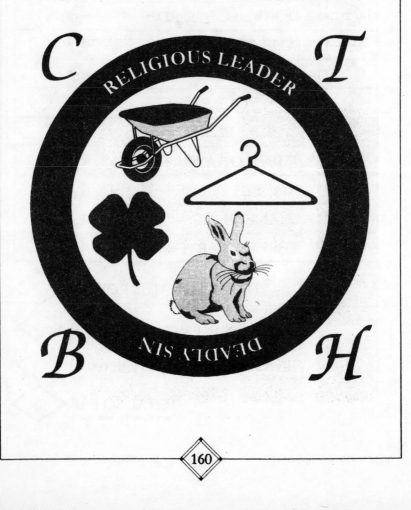

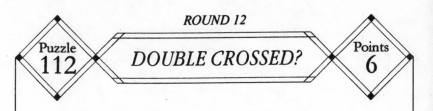

DOUBLE CROSSED?

"Have a look at this puzzle," says Lateral Larry. "There are eight crosses that need to be placed in this grid. As you can see, I've already done five of them for you.

"I want you to place the remaining three crosses in any of the boxes so that the number of crosses in every row, column and the two main diagonals is the same.

"Now, I can't make it any easier than that, can I?" he says, smiling.

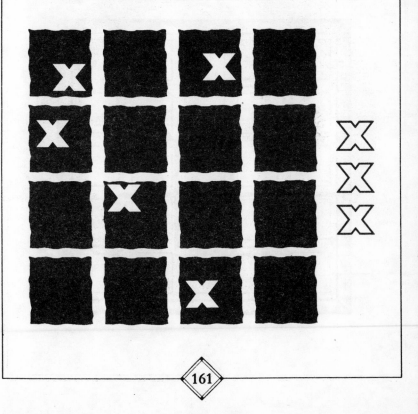

Baker Bill is setting out his food stall to feed the hungry fairground visitors. He has cookies, doughnuts, buns, pies and pizza slices – five of each. How can he arrange his wares so that the same item never appears in the same row, column or compartment?

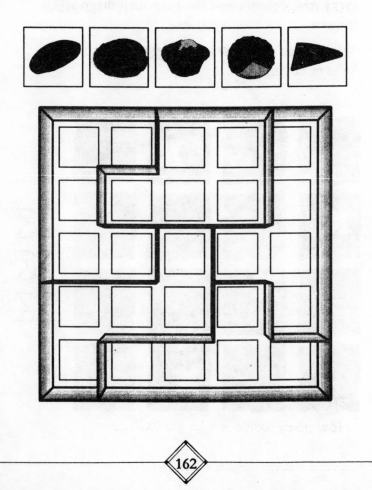

WORD RUNES

Mystic Molly has some more runes for use in the next challenge. "When I place the runes like this (see below) I consider this to read as ORES, in the usual left-to-right fashion, on the black ring.

"How many moves would it take for you to slide the runes from circle to circle so that the word EROS can be read in the same way?" she asks.

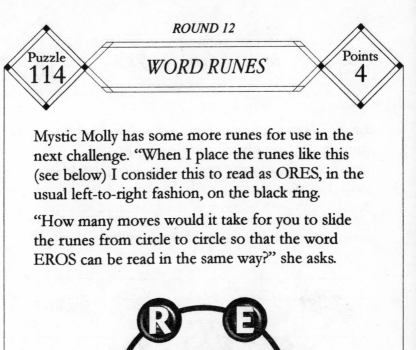

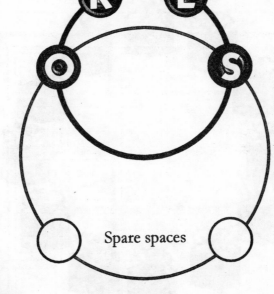

Spare spaces

 Solve this additional puzzle for 5 bonus points:

How many would it take for ROSE?

Sideshow Sid has a new game. "Here are twelve prizes. You and I take turns to take one prize or two consecutive prizes. The person to take the last prize wins them all."

Given that you have the choice of going first or second, what strategy should you employ?

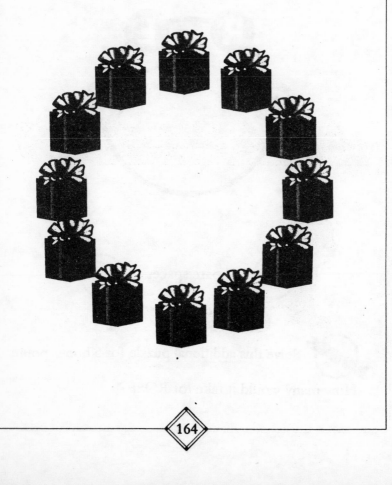

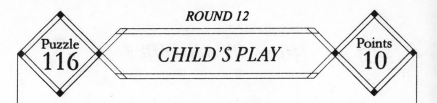

The letters blocks below are rather remarkable. Not only can they form three different 8-letter anagrams, but in addition these three words are all related to family life, childhood in particular.

First work out what these three words are. Then say which word can be spelled out from left to right using the fewest moves. A move consists of swapping a pair of letters in the row.

Mandy Math asks you to think of a number. "OK, now multiply it by four. Then add two. Finally, multiply the result by five. Now tell me what your total was."

Amazingly, as quick as a flash, she is able to tell you the number you first thought of.

What is the simplest rule that Mandy could use to work it out?

HOOPLA

What would you see if you looked at this hoopla
ring and cone from directions X and Y?

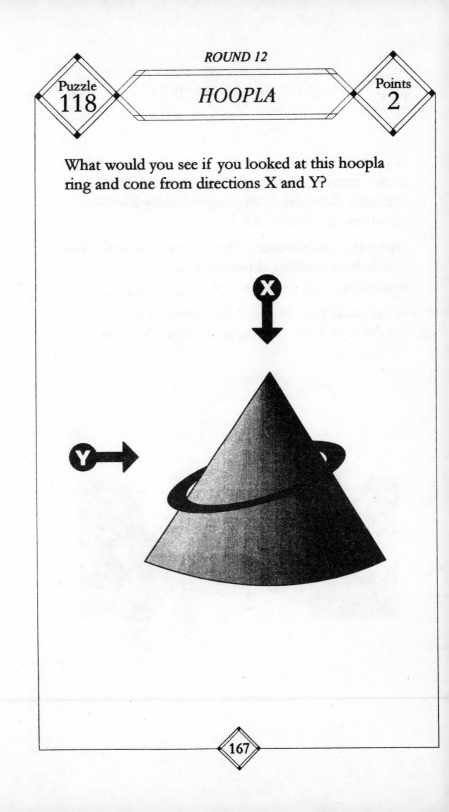

A group of girls have met up at the fairground for a class reunion. Everyone shakes hands with everyone else there. Two people shaking hands counts as one handshake.

Given that the number of people there is even, can you deduce anything about the number of handshakes that have taken place?

What could you say about the number of handshakes if the number of people there was a multiple of 4?

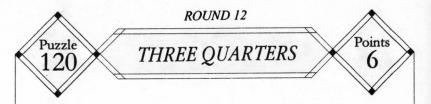

"Want to win some money?" asks Sideshow Sid. "Silly question I suppose," he says, "although there are a lot of conditions you must obey in this game.

"Here are three American quarters. You may touch and move the one on the left. You may touch but not move the middle coin. You may move but not touch the right-hand quarter. Got that?

"Now, I'll let you keep a coin if you can get it to pass to the right-hand side of the dotted line."

What would you do?

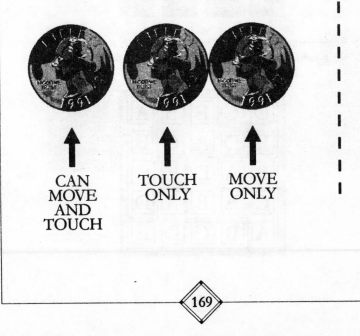

CAN
MOVE
AND
TOUCH

TOUCH
ONLY

MOVE
ONLY

111. The four words are B+ARROW, H+ANGER, RABBI+T and C+LOVER.

112. It soon becomes evident that you can't put three crosses in three different boxes to achieve the desired effect. However, as the title of the puzzle implies, if you put a "double cross" in one square, then there would be two crosses in every row, column, main diagonal (and even every quadrant of four squares).

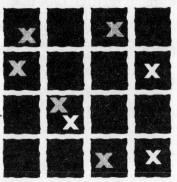

113. Representing the goodies with the letters A to E, the following pattern satisfies the criteria (there are other solutions):

ANSWERS

114. A simpler way of representing the rings is:

where circles 1 to 4 currently read ORES (the starting position) and circles 5 and 6 are spare. We can move a letter into any of the adjacent circles. We use the notation R1 to mean "Move the R into circle 1". To get EROS takes ten moves: S5, S6, O4, O5, E4, E1, O4, O3, S5 and S4. To get ROSE takes twelve moves: S5, S6, E4, E5, O4, O3, S1, S4, R1, O2, S3 and finally E4.

115. You choose to play second. Whatever prize(s) your opponent takes, you take the prize(s) on the opposite side of the circle. Whatever your opponent does destroys the symmetry of the circle, and whatever you do restores it. This forces your opponent to leave you with the last prize.

116. The words are PRENATAL, PARENTAL and PATERNAL. Of these, it only takes four swaps to get from the start position to PRENATAL:

117. Suppose the number you thought of was x. Multiplying by four then adding two gives us $4x+2$. Multiplying the result by five gives $5(4x+2)$. We need to rearrange this slightly:

$$5(4x + 2) = 20x + 10 = 10(2x + 1)$$

Therefore, to get back to x, Mandy takes your total, ignores the zero at the end, subtracts one, then halves the answer. For example, if your end total was 150, Mandy would think of 15 less 1 divided by 2 = 7.

118. View from X: View from Y:

119. You cannot deduce anything about the number of handshakes if the number of people is even. However, if the number of people is a multiple of 4, the number of handshakes must be even (but not necessarily a multiple of 4).

120. Press down on the middle coin with a finger from your right hand. Take the left-hand coin and slide it briskly toward the middle coin. The momentum will transfer through to the right-hand coin and shoot it over the line. (This principle is used in the Newton's Cradle executive toy.)

You can now pick up that quarter. And, because you can move and touch the left-hand coin, you can now move that one over the line by hand and pick that one up too!

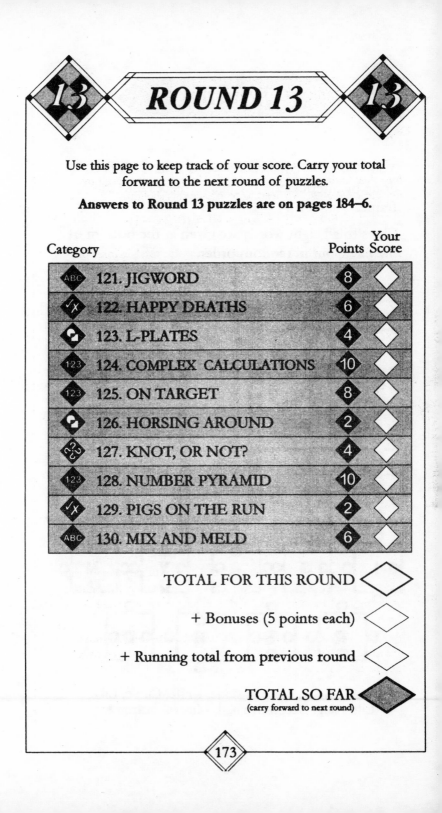

Use this page to keep track of your score. Carry your total forward to the next round of puzzles.

Answers to Round 13 puzzles are on pages 184–6.

Category	Points	Your Score
121. JIGWORD	8	◇
122. HAPPY DEATHS	6	◇
123. L-PLATES	4	◇
124. COMPLEX CALCULATIONS	10	◇
125. ON TARGET	8	◇
126. HORSING AROUND	2	◇
127. KNOT, OR NOT?	4	◇
128. NUMBER PYRAMID	10	◇
129. PIGS ON THE RUN	2	◇
130. MIX AND MELD	6	◇

TOTAL FOR THIS ROUND ◇

+ Bonuses (5 points each) ◇

+ Running total from previous round ◇

TOTAL SO FAR ◆
(carry forward to next round)

Your aim is to construct a word square. This is done by interlocking the jigsaw pieces into the frame.

Clues to all eight words are given at the bottom of the page, but in random order.

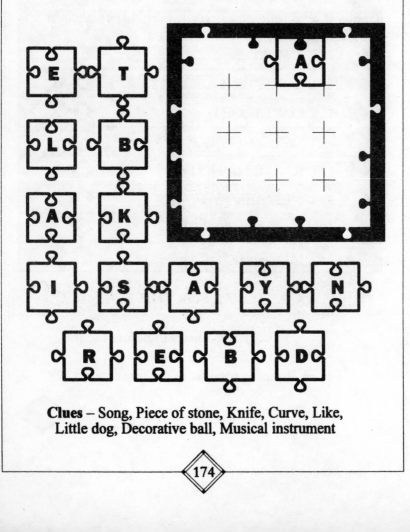

Clues – Song, Piece of stone, Knife, Curve, Like, Little dog, Decorative ball, Musical instrument

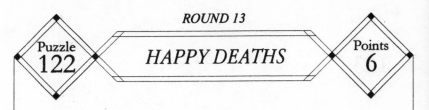

HAPPY DEATHS

"We've had many unwelcome visitors to the carnival," begins Lateral Larry. "Hugo was heading our way in 1989 but fortunately he died before reaching here.

"Likewise, Andrew was due to arrive a few years ago and the same fate befell him."

Can you work out why Larry is particularly pleased about these deaths?

Baker Bill uses L-shaped plates in his café. "They're brilliant for side orders!" he explains. He can place six plates on one table (which is covered by a checkerboard tablecloth), leaving a square in the middle.

How else can the plates be arranged so that a different square is left empty?

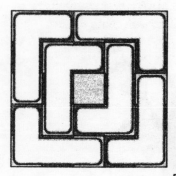

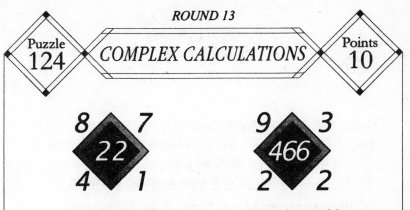

can be formed by   can be formed by

$(87 + 1) \div 4 = 22$ $932 \div 2 = 466$

Note that, in the examples above, the digits are used in clockwise order. What calculation can represented by the following?

 Solve this additional puzzle for 5 bonus points:

What is the OTHER solution to the above question?

Sideshow Sid has a game of skill for visitors to his stall. Contenders are allowed three throws of a dart. They win a prize if all three throws hit the dartboard and the total forms a prime number.

What chance would you have of winning, given that your darts were thrown at random but all hit the board?

The three areas shown are of equal size.

 Solve this additional puzzle for 5 bonus points:

How many different total scores are there under these circumstances?

HORSING AROUND

How can the white knight reach the finish square in the fewest possible moves? Throughout the journey, it must not land on a square where it could be captured by one of the black pieces.

FINISH

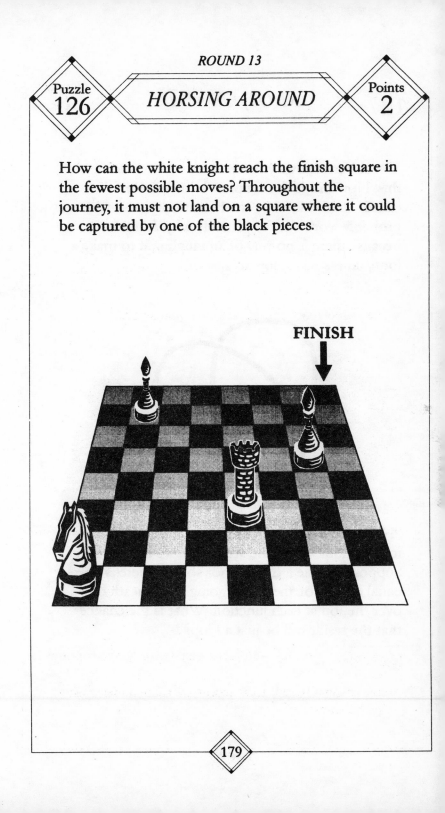

Visual Vern shows you a picture. "Have a look at this. Now this is the simplest knot known. It's called a trefoil knot by mathematicians, and you can probably work out for yourself why. It is a knot because there is no way of untangling it to make a loop, unless you resort to scissors.

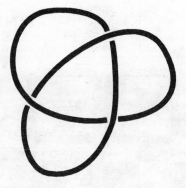

"Now, you'll notice that the knot has three intersections where the string crosses itself. Suppose I make a trefoil knot so that there is an equal chance of the string going underneath or over the top at each junction. What is the chance that the result will be just a loop?"

NUMBER PYRAMID

By taking bricks one-by-one from the top of the pile, form a correct sum.

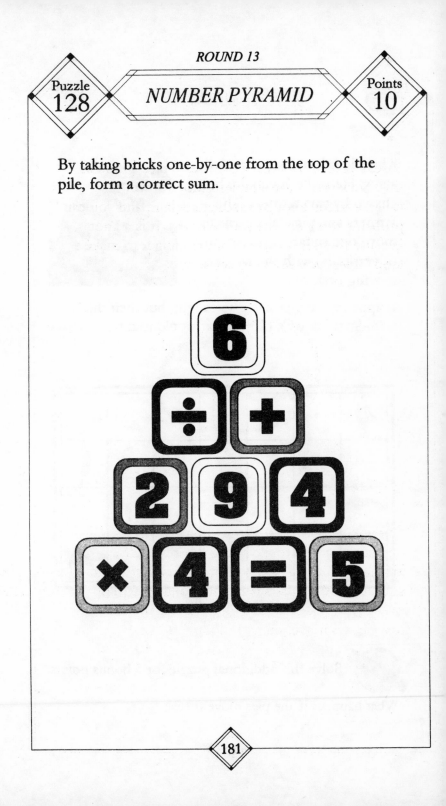

PIGS ON THE RUN

This pig is looking particularly smug. He and a friend are being chased by two farmers. The farmers and pigs take turns to move one square (horizontally or vertically) with the farmers moving first.

It appears the pigs can't be caught, but then the farmers think of a ploy. What would that be?

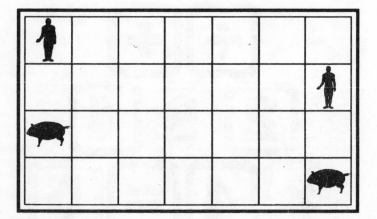

 Solve this additional puzzle for 5 bonus points:

What happens if the pigs move first?

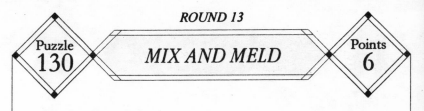

Wordsmith Will has another of his verbal puzzles. "Not too hard, this one," he says. "All you have to do is take two of the words in each line and anagram them to form a synonym of the third word.

"I'll even give you a head start. The answer to the first row is FOLKLORE (ROOK + FELL) which means the same as MYTH."

ROOK	**MYTH**	**FELL**
COIN	LOUD	BOON
RIDS	**SETS**	**FEAR**
MAIL	DRAG	SONG
KISS	**STAR**	**RATE**
OVAL	**TILL**	**EPIC**

121.

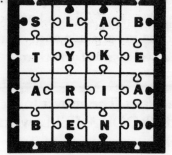

122. Andrew and Hugo were hurricanes.

123. It is possible to leave any one of the four corner squares uncovered, like so:

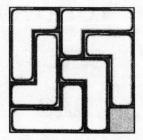

124. First of all, you must establish that, in addition to the four basic mathematical operations, concatenation (that is, placing two or more digits side-by-side) is also allowed. The two possible solutions are:

$$384 \div 2 = 192$$
$$3 \times 8 \times 4 \times 2 = 192$$

ANSWERS

125. 1-in-27. There are three possibilities for each of the three darts, leading to twenty-seven different, equally likely permutations. Suppose all three darts land in the "1" zone. This totals 3, a prime number. If one, two or all three darts move into another segment this would add 3 or 6 per dart to the score. No matter what the exact details, this would mean the total would then be divisible by 3. Hence, 1+1+1 is the only prime total out of the 27. Bonus answer: There are seven different scores.

126. The easiest way to solve this is to cross out all the squares which are being attacked by a black piece and then work out your possibilities from the Finish back to the Start:

FINISH

127. There are 2 × 2 × 2 = 8 possibilities. Of these, only two are knots. This occurs when the string always goes over the top, or always goes underneath itself, as you follow the string around the loop.

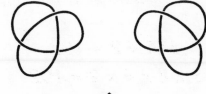

128. The correct sequence is:

129. The farmers decide each to chase the other's pig, then swap pigs once they're caught. Interestingly, if the pigs move first, it isn't an advantage to them. In fact, it allows each farmer to collect his own pig. This is because the farmer can back the pig into a corner then force it to move into a square where he can catch it.

130. The answers are:

ROOK + FELL = FOLKLORE (MYTH)
LOUD + BOON = DOUBLOON (COIN)
RIDS + SETS = DISTRESS (FEAR)
DRAG + MAIL = MADRIGAL (SONG)
KISS + RATE = ASTERISK (STAR)
TILL + EPIC = ELLIPTIC (OVAL)

ROUND 14

Use this page to keep track of your score. Carry your total forward to the next round of puzzles.

Answers to Round 14 puzzles are on pages 198–200.

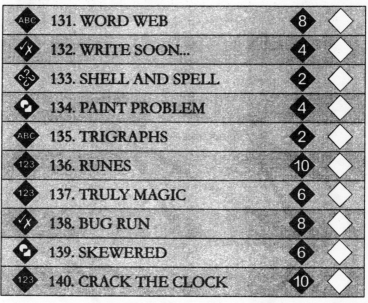

Category	Points	Your Score
131. WORD WEB	8	◇
132. WRITE SOON...	4	◇
133. SHELL AND SPELL	2	◇
134. PAINT PROBLEM	4	◇
135. TRIGRAPHS	2	◇
136. RUNES	10	◇
137. TRULY MAGIC	6	◇
138. BUG RUN	8	◇
139. SKEWERED	6	◇
140. CRACK THE CLOCK	10	◇

TOTAL FOR THIS ROUND ◇

+ Bonuses (5 points each) ◇

+ Running total from previous round ◇

TOTAL SO FAR ◆
(carry forward to next round)

There are three 7-letter words that can be made
with the letters E, H, N, O, R, S and T. Place them
in the diagram so that any of the three words can
be traced from circle to circle without skipping any
letters.

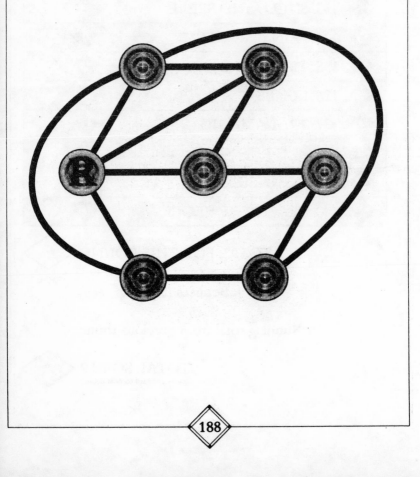

WRITE SOON...

A man was writing a large message, slowly and carefully, to welcome visitors to the carnival.

Unfortunately, a large storm was brewing and he had to stop just as he was halfway through a letter. Although this was a shame, his life would have been in some danger if he had not stopped.

In what circumstances do you think this happened?

Spell out the names of three shells. The letters spiral towards the outside.

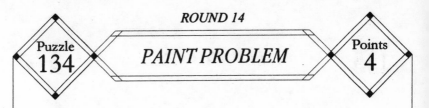

PAINT PROBLEM

Colin the Clown has a square window in his caravan which is 3 feet wide. Unfortunately Daft Dennis, his room mate, wants to paint half the area of the window with blue paint.

"Don't do that," pleads Colin, "I like the window the way it is."

Dennis calms Colin down. "Don't be silly. Once I've finished you'll will still have a square window 3 feet high and 3 feet wide."

How can this be achieved?

Using the clues provided (which are in no particular order), complete all the words. Each word is the only word in the English language to contain the sequences of three letters shown.

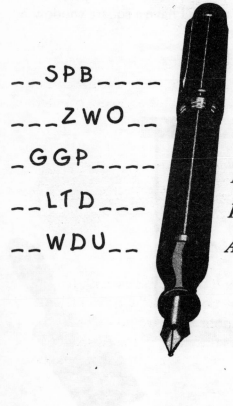

_ _ S P B _ _ _ _

_ _ _ Z W O _ _

_ G G P _ _ _ _

_ _ L T D _ _ _

_ _ W D U _ _

Clues:

Critical failure

Shavings

Piece of jargon

Fruit

Aubergine

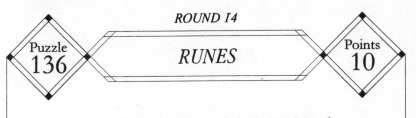

"I need your help for this puzzle," says Mandy Math. "If I join together three dots on a circle, I can only make one shape – a triangle.

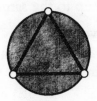

"If I use four dots, I can make three different shapes. To keep things simple, we'll say that shapes that are the same except for a rotation are counted as different.

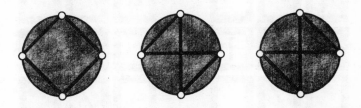

"I'll also tell you that if I do the same with five dots, there are twelve possibilities. Can you tell me how many combinations there would be, still counting rotations as different, if I used six dots?"

TRULY MAGIC

"Roll up, roll up for my latest confounding number puzzle," exclaims Lateral Larry. "Challengers must complete the magic square so that nine consecutive integers have been used and every row, column and both diagonals add up to the same value.

"To win my game, you must provide two different answers. I've started you off. As a free hint, I'll tell you that the totals in each square will need to be different."

 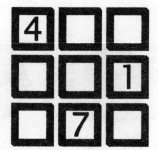

 Solve this additional puzzle for 5 bonus points:

How many other solutions are there?

BUG RUN

The children in the Animals Corner were watching the antics of Bob the Bug. He wants to get over to the other bank but his movements need to be surprisingly logical (for a bug).

Each symbol represents a different direction (either left, right, up or down) and these decide where Bob must move next.

Can you work out the directions the symbols represent given that Bob was able to cross the chasm without standing on a skull square?

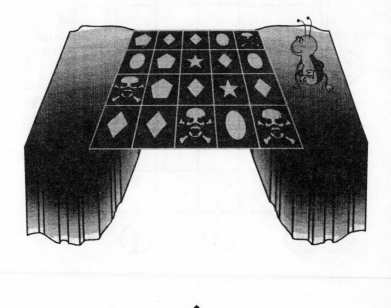

Baker Bill is setting up his barbecue. He is heating up a number of skewers. The skewers come in different lengths, so each one crosses the path of several other skewers, as shown by the numbers on the diagram.

Can you use logic to deduce how the skewers must be arranged?

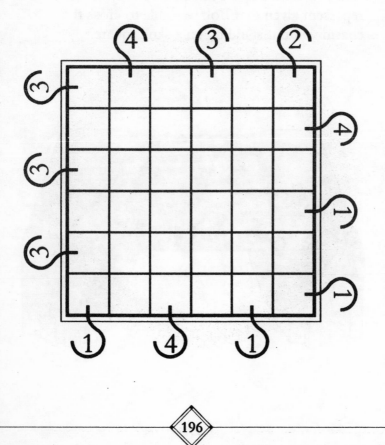

CRACK THE CLOCK

Using any number of straight lines, it is possible to divide up the clock face so that each section between the lines adds up to the same total.

How many different totals can be formed in this way?

131. The words are HORNETS, THRONES and SHORTEN. You can deduce that the H will need to be in a circle with four connectors because it must be next to the O, T, R and S (looking at where H appears in the words above). Repeating this for the other letters greatly reduces the combinations possible.

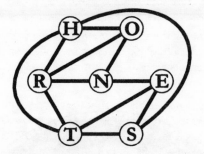

132. The man was a skywriter.

133. RAZOR, SCALLOP and CONCH can be read.

134. Dennis painted four triangular areas, as shown:

135. The words are RASPBERRY, BUZZWORD, EGGPLANT, MELTDOWN, SAWDUST.

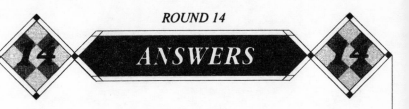

ANSWERS

136. The answer is 60. Suppose we draw a diagram from points 1, 3, 4, 6, 5, 2 (and back to 1). This diagram would look the same if we had chosen 6, 5, 2, 1, 3, 4 (and back to 6) because we have just used a different start/finish point for the same sequence. So we need only concern ourselves with how we choose five points in the route. At first there are five points to choose from, then four, then three etc. So there are $5 \times 4 \times 3 \times 2 \times 1 = 120$ routes.

Diagrams also look the same if we reverse the route. Hence we get the answer $120 / 2 = 60$. For n points, the number of possible diagrams is given by the formula $(n - 1)! / 2$.

137. There are two possible solutions (and hence the answer to Bonus question is "None"). The key to the puzzle lies in "consecutive integers", which permits the use of negatives. By trying different possibilities for the middle number, one can deduce that the numbers 0 to 8 cannot form a magic square with a total of 12 (although you can get very close – a diagonal line adding up to 15 spoils it).

Total = 15   Total = 9

138. Up = Star, Down = Pentagon, Left = Diamond, Right = Oval. This permits the following route:

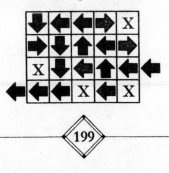

139.

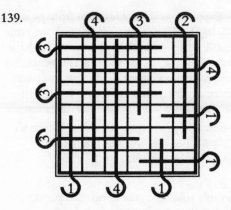

140. The secret is to exploit the symmetry of the clock and pair up the numbers into 13s. There are three possible configurations, giving totals of 13, 26 and 39:

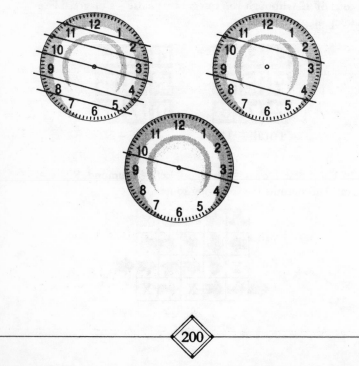

ROUND 15

Use this page to keep track of your score. Carry your total forward to the next round of puzzles.

Answers to Round 15 puzzles are on pages 212–14.

Category		Points	Your Score
ABC	141. WORD GRID	4	◇
⊕	142. DON'T BELIEVE IT	6	◇
⟨?⟩	143. STREET PLAN	8	◇
123	144. NEW DEAL	6	◇
⊕	145. ROLL OVER	10	◇
✓✗	146. LETTER SHOT	10	◇
123	147. NUMBER JIG	2	◇
ABC	148. WORD ASSOCIATION	2	◇
⊕	149. WIN THE WINE	8	◇
✓✗	150. NOT A-LLOWED	4	◇

TOTAL FOR THIS ROUND ◇

+ Bonuses (5 points each) ◇

+ Running total from previous round ◇

TOTAL SO FAR ◆
(carry forward to next round)

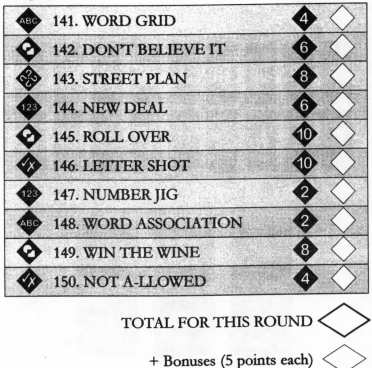

To win the game, use the letter pairs provided so that nine 4-letter words are made in the completed 3×3 grid. The same letter pair may not appear twice in any row or column.

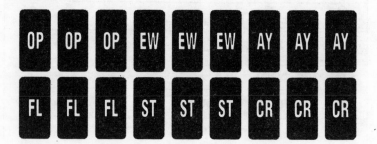

"One of these hexagonal boxes contains a prize. But I'll let you into a secret," confides Lateral Larry. "Three arrows allow you to reduce the number of possibilities to a prime number. The fourth arrow is not needed and should be ignored."

Can you work out which arrow is unnecessary and therefore which boxes haven't been discounted?

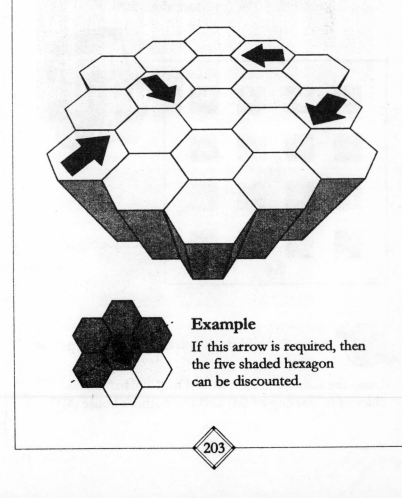

Example

If this arrow is required, then the five shaded hexagon can be discounted.

Chester the Taxi Driver is due to drive from (A) to the carnival (C) to pick up some of the fairground's visitors and take them home. However, he would dearly love to stop off at his house (H) for a quick cup of coffee first.

How many of the 70 shortest routes from (A) to (C) pass by his house? Choose from: (a) Less than 50%, (b) Exactly 50%, (c) More than 50%.

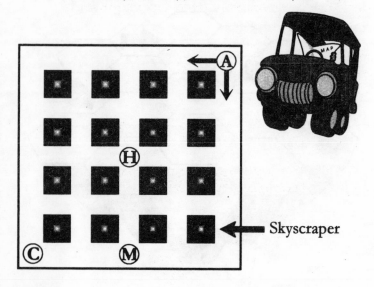

Skyscraper

 Solve this additional puzzle for 5 bonus points:

Using the same journey from (A) to (C), what are his chances of passing by (H) **and** his mother's house (M)?

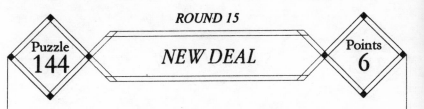

NEW DEAL

Marvin the Magician has just shuffled a deck of the thirteen Hearts cards. "Watch this," he says. He deals three cards from the pack, face down. "Turn them over," he asks.

As you do so, you reveal the Two, Nine and Queen of Hearts. "Notice that they are in ascending order of value. Now I'll deal out five cards this time." He replaces the three cards in the deck, shuffles it, and deals five cards onto the table, keeping them face down for the moment.

What are the odds that these cards have been dealt in ascending order?

ROLL OVER

Which two of these "nets" could Mandy Math glue together to give her two standard gambling dice?

Don't worry about the orientation of the dots.

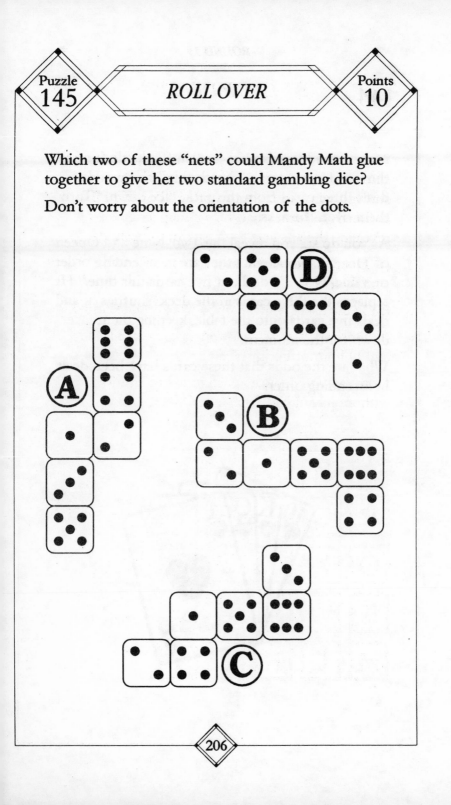

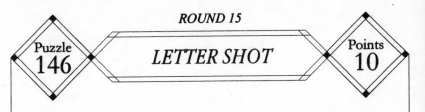

LETTER SHOT

Sideshow Sid runs a darts stall. One of the lettered cards has a prize on the other side. Hit that card and you win. Sid makes an offer: "For $50 I'll indirectly tell you what the winning letter is by revealing the answers to these three questions:

(a) Does the letter live in the first half of the alphabet?

(b) Is the letter is made up of straight lines only?

(c) Does the letter's shape enclose an area (as in Q and D but not H nor N)?"

How can you deduce which target to aim for without paying Sid a single cent?

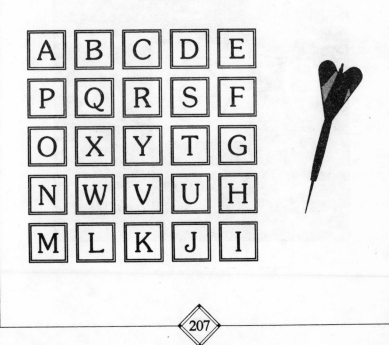

This number jigsaw shows two ways of reaching the number 12.

Suppose the plus sign is changed to another multiplication sign. How could you rearrange the pieces so that the jigsaw is mathematically correct once again?

WORD ASSOCIATION

What word would logically fit in the middle box?

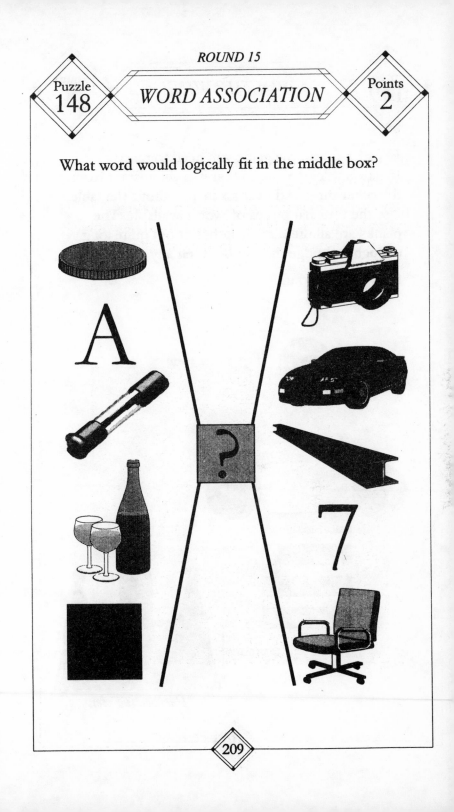

In order to win the game you need to place a
fourth bottle of wine so that it is equidistant from
the other three and over six inches above the table.
Use the four flat pieces of wood available. The
planks are all the same length, but not quite long
enough to bridge the gap between any two bottles.

How do you do it?

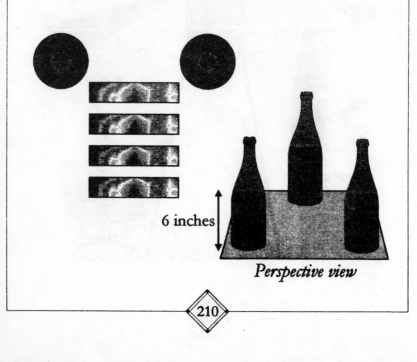

Top-down view

6 inches

Perspective view

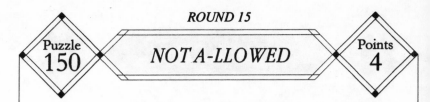

Puzzle
150

NOT A-LLOWED

Points
4

"I once appeared on a game show," boasts Lateral Larry. "I was in the final round and was feeling pretty confident. That was until the question master read out the Big Prize question.

"He said, 'You have one minute to name one hundred words which do not contain the letter A.' My first reaction was 'How on earth am I supposed to do that?' But after thinking for a few seconds, I managed to win the prize."

Can you work out Larry's answer?

141. FL, ST and CR can be used as prefixes for any of OP, EW and AY, giving the following nine words:

FL OP	ST EW	CR AY
FL OP	ST EW	CR AY
CR EW	FL AY	ST OP
ST AY	CR OP	FL EW

142. The arrow on the far right is unnecessary. This leaves three boxes to choose from. (If you choose any other arrow as the false one, you leave yourself with six boxes, which isn't prime.)

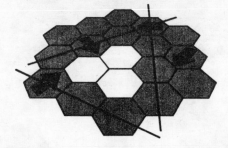

143. There are six routes from A to H. There are six routes from H to C. So there are 6 × 6 = 36 routes from A to C via H. Hence the chance is 36/70, which is just over 50% so (c) is correct.

Bonus puzzle: 6/70, because there are only 6 routes from A to C via H and M. When he gets to H there is only one shortest route from H to C via M.

ANSWERS

144. There are $5 \times 4 \times 3 \times 2 \times 1 = 120$ ways of ordering the cards. Of these, only one has the cards appearing in ascending order. So the answer is 1-in-120.

145. B and C are correct, because their opposite sides will add up to the traditional seven. In A, the 5 and 6 are transposed. In D, 1 and 2 are transposed.

146. "A" is the answer. It is given that you narrow down the field to one if you know the answers to the questions. We can see that the winning letter must be the one that is alone in its box.

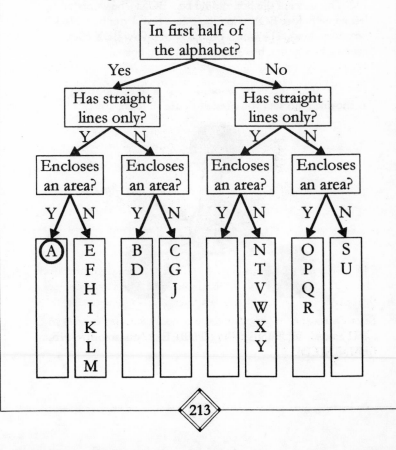

147. Although you can't use the usual trick of turning the 6 and 9 upside down, there's no reason why you can't swap the pieces over. This gives $2 \times 9 = 18 = 6 \times 3$.

148. The word in the box should be... BOX! The words on the left come before BOX (Coin box, fuse box, letter box, black box, wine box). The words on the right follow BOX (Box camera, box girder, box number, box seat, box car).

149. Use three pieces of wood to make a self-supporting bridge, as shown. Who said you needed to use all four?

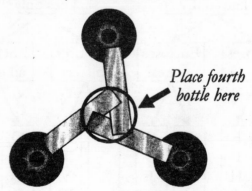

Place fourth bottle here

150. Larry said, "ONE, TWO, THREE ... (and so on), ONE HUNDRED!"

TEST YOUR STRENGTH

How are you doing? Calculate your score so far and
see how high you can try...

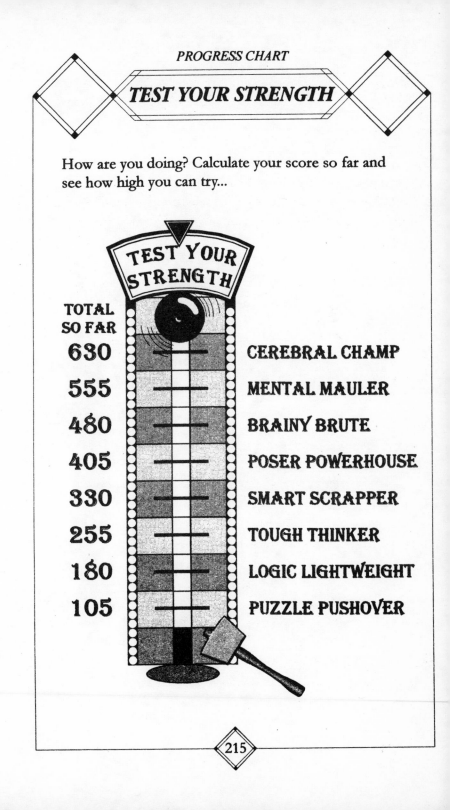

TOTAL SO FAR	
630	CEREBRAL CHAMP
555	MENTAL MAULER
480	BRAINY BRUTE
405	POSER POWERHOUSE
330	SMART SCRAPPER
255	TOUGH THINKER
180	LOGIC LIGHTWEIGHT
105	PUZZLE PUSHOVER

Use this page to keep track of your score. Carry your total forward to the next round of puzzles.

Answers to Round 16 puzzles are on pages 228–30.

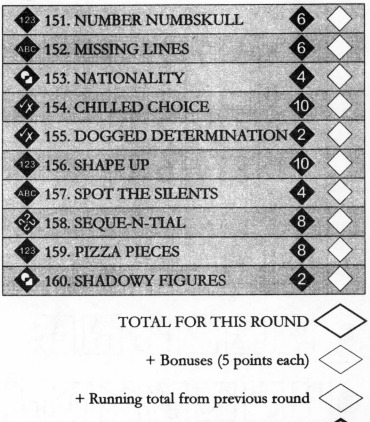

Category	Points	Your Score
151. NUMBER NUMBSKULL	6	
152. MISSING LINES	6	
153. NATIONALITY	4	
154. CHILLED CHOICE	10	
155. DOGGED DETERMINATION	2	
156. SHAPE UP	10	
157. SPOT THE SILENTS	4	
158. SEQUE-N-TIAL	8	
159. PIZZA PIECES	8	
160. SHADOWY FIGURES	2	

TOTAL FOR THIS ROUND

+ Bonuses (5 points each)

+ Running total from previous round

TOTAL SO FAR
(carry forward to next round)

The code grid contains 16 mathematical symbols. Use it to decode the three sums below. For example, if a box contains A and D, it must represent either a 1 or 8.

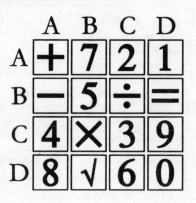

     A B C D

A + 7 2 1

B − 5 ÷ =

C 4 × 3 9

D 8 √ 6 0

① $\begin{array}{c}A\\C\end{array}$ $\begin{array}{c}B\\D\end{array}$ $\begin{array}{c}A\\D\end{array}$ C^B $\begin{array}{c}D\\B\end{array}$ C_A

② B^A $\begin{array}{c}A\\A\end{array}$ C_A $\begin{array}{c}B\\D\end{array}$ $\begin{array}{c}A\\D\end{array}$ $\begin{array}{c}A\\D\end{array}$

③ $\begin{array}{c}D\\C\end{array}$ $\begin{array}{c}B\\C\end{array}$ C_C $\begin{array}{c}A\\B\end{array}$ D_C B_D D^C

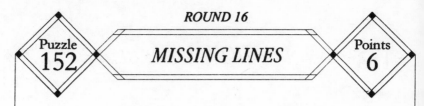

Puzzle
152

MISSING LINES

Points
6

These circular stones contain some symbols. Add four straight lines to make a 9-letter word. (You are not allowed to rearrange the stones.)

C I O P I F I F D

 Solve this additional puzzle for 5 bonus points:

If that puzzle was too easy, add five lines (one of which is curved) to make an 8-letter word. You are not allowed to change the order of the stones.

P A C I F P I V

At the entrance to the carnival there are a number of flags which welcome visitors from foreign lands.

These three flags are quite unusual, in that they spell out the names of the countries. Can you work out why these countries have been grouped together in this way?

FRANCE ITALY
IRELAND PERU

GERMANY BOLIVIA
HOLLAND HUNGARY

SWEDEN ICELAND
DENMARK NORWAY

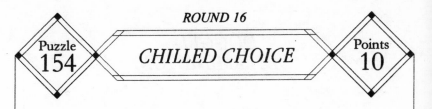

Puzzle
154

CHILLED CHOICE

Points
10

You need to place ice-creams in this rack. There are three sorts of ice-cream – vanilla, strawberry and chocolate. There are also three types of cone – standard, sugar, and chocolate-coated. There is one of every possible type, making nine ice-creams in all.

The same type of ice-cream or cone doesn't appear twice in any row or column.

The stall holder knows where each ice-cream should go, and you can point to a position in the grid and ask "Which sort of ice-cream goes here?" or "What type of cone lives here?"

What is the maximum number of questions you'd need to ask so that you know where to position all the ice-creams?

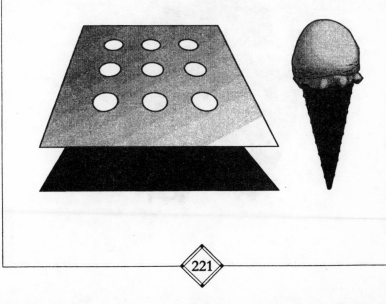

As Chaz was riding the rollercoaster, his watch fell off his wrist. Luckily, he managed to find it. Unfortunately, it landed five yards away from a vicious dog tied by a ten-yard rope to a pole. No matter how quickly he tried to dodge, the dog followed him step-for-step.

There was no way Chaz was going to try to push past the dog – he looked a bit too hungry for that! But after a little thought, he was easily able to retrieve his watch.

How did he manage it?

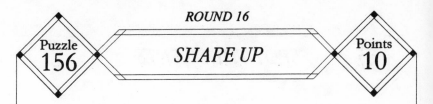

SHAPE UP

These nine symbols can be ordered in a certain sequence so that a mathematical progression, using the four basic arithmetic signs in turn, is formed.

However, in addition, the sequence also possesses two other forms of logic which will help you in the construction.

Free hint: Start with the circled 3. Also, the number 3 is used in the logic for the number series.

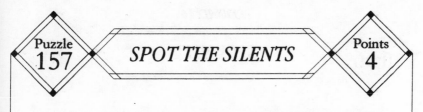

SPOT THE SILENTS

Puzzle 157 · Points 4

Each of these words contains a silent letter (such as the 'P' in PSALM). Pick out the silent letter in each case and you'll spell out a popular item at parties.

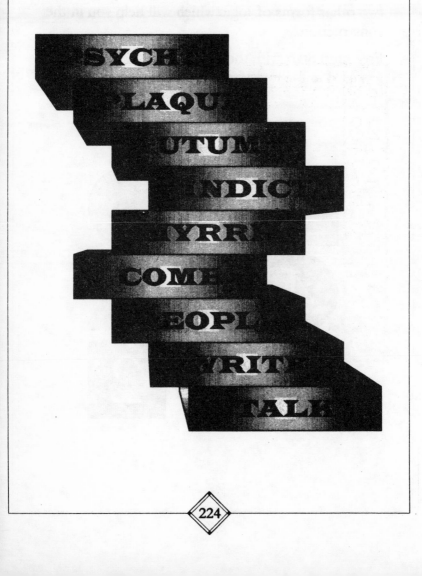

SEQUE-N-TIAL

Can you fathom out the logic of this series and thus provide the next number in the sequence?

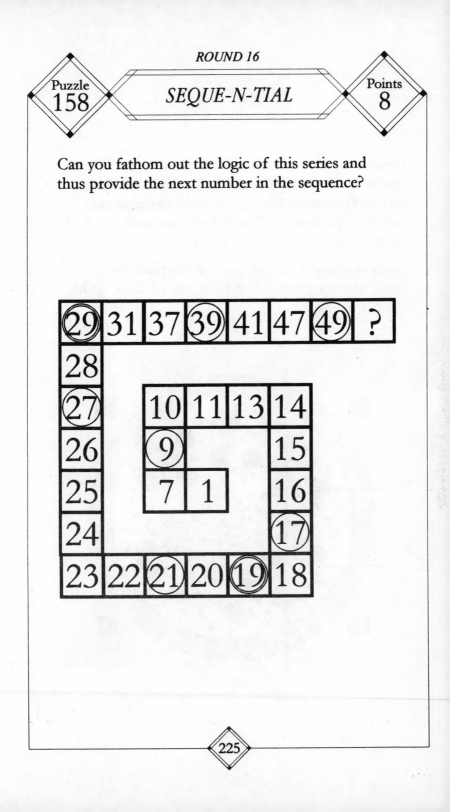

Brothers Alberto and Luigi are about to eat their pizza. Unlike most people, they prefer to eat the crust. They make two cuts at right angles to one another, as shown below. Alberto will take pieces A and C; Luigi gets pieces B and D.

In how many ways can they cut the pizza so that each brother gets the same amount of crust on his pieces of pizza?

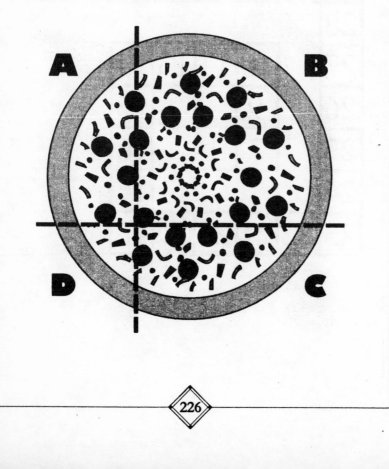

SHADOWY FIGURES

Visitors to the fairground can have their silhouette cut out in a piece of black paper for a small sum. Unfortunately, these silhouettes of a man and a woman have been cut up into pieces by accident.

Can you say which pieces belong to the man's silhouette?

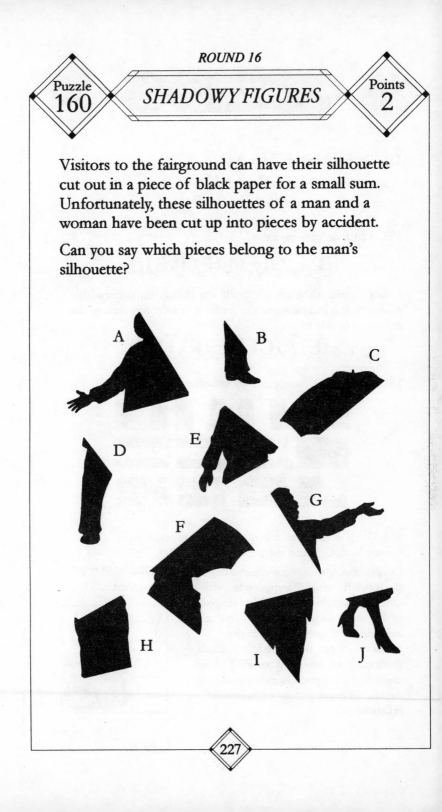

151. The equations are: $4 = 8 \div \sqrt{4}$
$$7 + 4 = 11$$
$$(6 \times 3) - 9 = 9$$

152. Add four lines to make:

Bonus puzzle: Although you could not change the order of the stones, in <u>this</u> puzzle there was nothing to stop you turning the last stone upside down!

153. The flags of each group of countries are very similar:

154. You'd need to ask five questions. Let's represent the ice-creams by S, C, V and the cone types as 1, 2, 3.

Concentrating on the ice-creams first, we ask "What kind is in the top-left corner?" Suppose the stall-holder says vanilla. The other two vanillas are on either diagonal of the shaded square. In the worst-case scenario, we'd need to ask for the positions of two other, different, kinds (because if we asked "What kind of ice-cream?" for a square already containing vanilla, we don't get any extra helpful information).

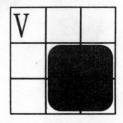

ANSWERS

Once we know the positions of three kinds of ice-cream, we can always fill in all nine (using the rule that no two kinds appear in the same row or column).

Now we concentrate on the cone types. Suppose the vanillas were on the top-left to bottom-right diagonal. Satisfy yourself that the same type of cone must run down the opposite main diagonal. For example, suppose we ask "What cone is in the top-right box?" and the answer is 1, then there must be 1's along the diagonal shown.

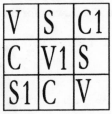

Asking "What cone is in this square?" for one of the remaining squares is enough for you to complete the grid.

155. Chaz walks around the dog in circles. As he does so, the dog will follow him. After a number of revolutions, the dog's rope should have wound around the pole and hence the dog's reach becomes short enough for Chaz to pick up his watch.

156. There are three sequences here. The arithmetic one is "multiply by 3, add 3, divide by 3, subtract 3...". There is also the "circle, square, triangle...." series, and the "white, black..." series:

157. The word formed is PUNCHBOWL.

158. The next number is 51. These are all the numbers which contain the letter N when spelled out (oNe, seveN etc.) A circle is put around numbers containing two Ns (NiNe, seveNteeN etc.), or a double circle for three Ns (NiNeteeN, tweNty-NiNe).

159. Believe it or not, any two cuts at right angles would do. For example, if you moved the horizontal cut upward, you would be reducing the amount of crust in A but adding just as much back in C. Likewise for B and D.

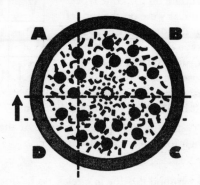

160. Pieces A, B, D, G and I make up the man; the others make up the woman with the umbrella.

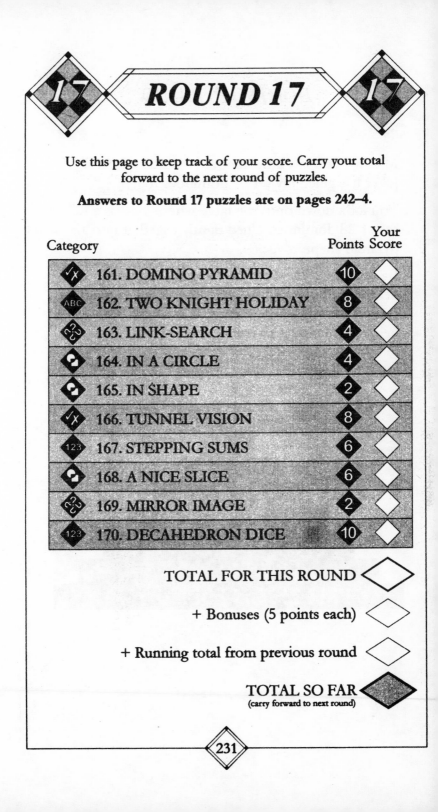

ROUND 17

Use this page to keep track of your score. Carry your total forward to the next round of puzzles.

Answers to Round 17 puzzles are on pages 242–4.

Category	Points	Your Score
161. DOMINO PYRAMID	10	◇
162. TWO KNIGHT HOLIDAY	8	◇
163. LINK-SEARCH	4	◇
164. IN A CIRCLE	4	◇
165. IN SHAPE	2	◇
166. TUNNEL VISION	8	◇
167. STEPPING SUMS	6	◇
168. A NICE SLICE	6	◇
169. MIRROR IMAGE	2	◇
170. DECAHEDRON DICE	10	◇

TOTAL FOR THIS ROUND ◇

+ Bonuses (5 points each) ◇

+ Running total from previous round ◇

TOTAL SO FAR ◆
(carry forward to next round)

DOMINO PYRAMID

Mandy Math is a little annoyed. "Some practical joker has glued my set of dominoes together."

You look down onto the table where there is a full set of 28 dominoes, glued tightly together into a pyramid shape.

By looking at the diagram carefully, can you determine how the tiles were assembled so that you can tell Mandy where she needs to chisel her beloved dominoes apart?

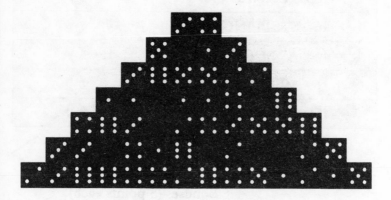

Wordsmith Will is playing with his chess pieces when he offers you a challenge.

"Suppose I place the white and black knights here. If you were to move the black knight eight times you would spell out the name of an 8-letter country."

Which country?

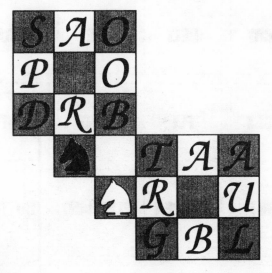

 Solve this additional puzzle for 5 bonus points:

The same thing can be done with the white knight. Which country does it spell out in 8 moves?

The words in the grid below have been circled because they can all be associated with the word "BLUE". Using similar associations, circle other groups into lines of three or four words.

Which groups are formed, and which word is left out?

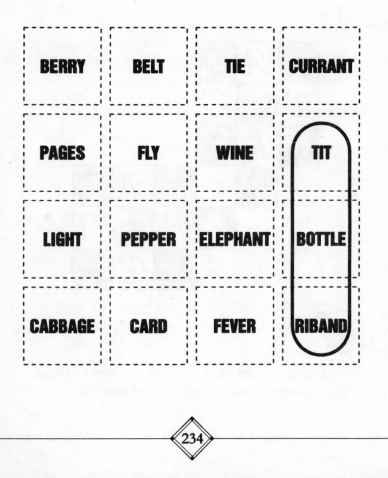

BERRY	BELT	TIE	CURRANT
PAGES	FLY	WINE	TIT
LIGHT	PEPPER	ELEPHANT	BOTTLE
CABBAGE	CARD	FEVER	RIBAND

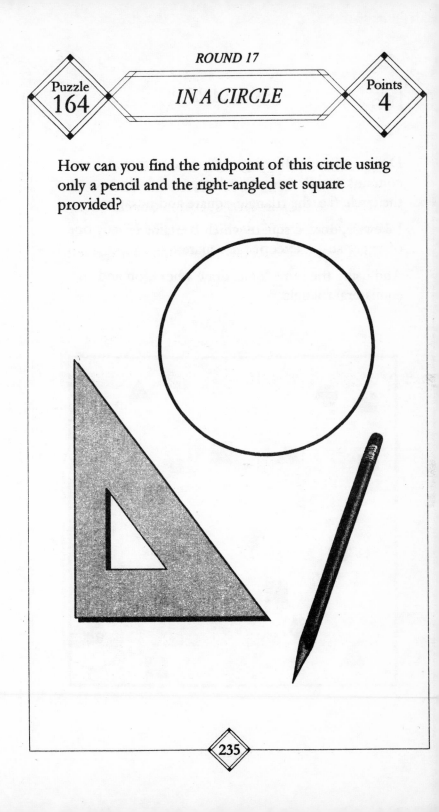

How can you find the midpoint of this circle using only a pencil and the right-angled set square provided?

Draw a circle in the diagram below so that it contains exactly one of each type of shape **except** the circle (i.e. the triangle, square and hexagon).

Likewise, draw a square which contains exactly one of every shape **except** the square.

And using the same logic, draw a hexagon and an equilateral triangle.

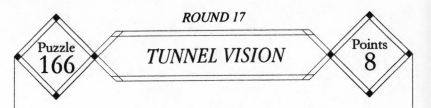

TUNNEL VISION

Lateral Larry relates one of his stories. "I was once in the army and one night we decided to have a night on the town. Unfortunately, the only way out of the underground camp was through a long tunnel which took ten minutes to travel, even if you ran.

"Worse still, there was a guard who would come out of his hut every five minutes to check that no one was escaping, and to send back anyone arriving without the correct papers.

"Luckily, we thought of a way to get around the problem, although we had some explaining to do when we got back!"

How did Larry and his pals go AWOL for the night?

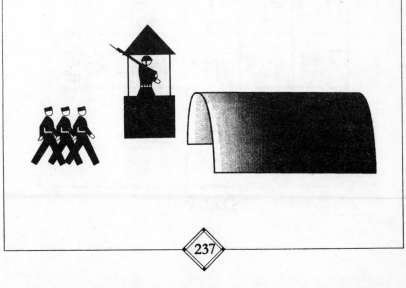

Mandy Math has made a new game for her Number Cruncher carnival stall. Contestants start on the square indicated and must jump from square to square using a mathematical sequence.

On getting to the Finish square, the contestant must then choose one of nine prizes, numbered from 1 to 9.

What route should you take, and what prize would you opt for? (At one place along the route it is necessary to "skip" over a square to continue the sequence.)

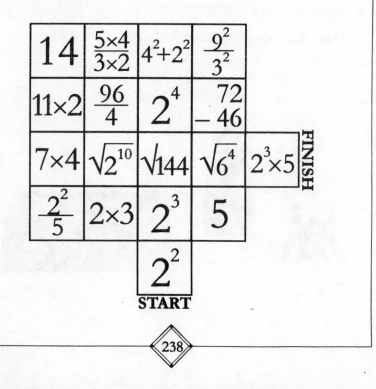

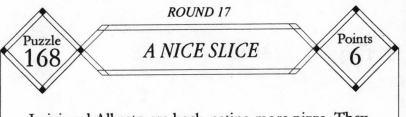

A NICE SLICE

Luigi and Alberto are back, eating more pizza. They have already eaten three of the pizzas from the tray. Now they want to put a straight slice right through the tray so that it divides the pizzas fairly.

One solution is a horizontal slice through the tray. How else could you cut the pizzas to ensure the areas on either side of the cut are equal?

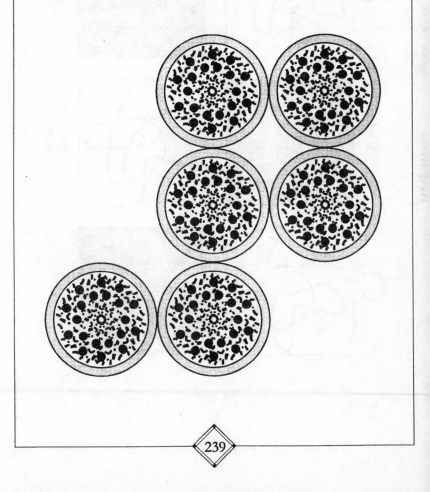

MIRROR IMAGE

Match up the ropes (A, B, C) with their mirror images (1, 2, 3).

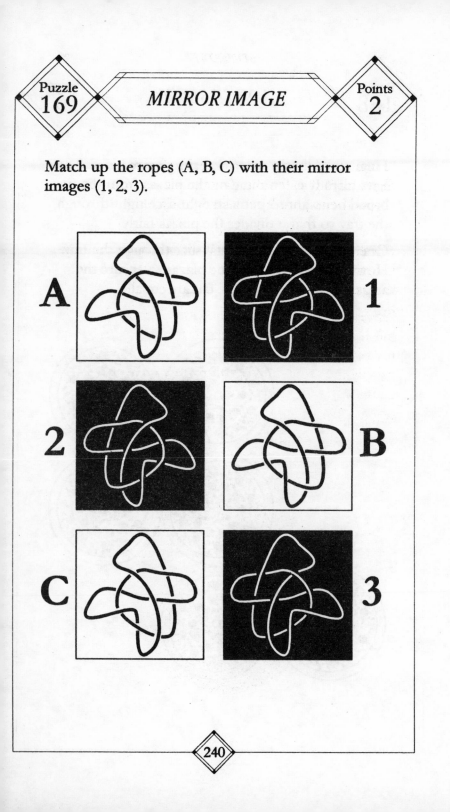

Puzzle
170

DECAHEDRON DICE

Points
10

"Here are three ten-sided dice. Each one has the digits from 0 to 9 on its faces made up of 10 equal-shaped pentagons," explains Mandy Math.

"I have two of the dice and you take the third. We roll the three dice together. If the value on your die is between the two values on my dice then you win the game.

"It's no good if your die equals one of my dice – it has to be precisely between the two values. So, if my two dice come up with consecutive numbers or exactly the same number, I'm sure to win that game."

What do you reckon your percentage chance of winning this gamble is?

161. This is easier than it looks. Every square must be accounted for. So, if you examine the corner dominoes these must be horizontal (otherwise squares would have to be omitted). Likewise for every domino up the sides, as shown below. This leaves you with a smaller pyramid for which the same applies. So all the dominoes were glued together horizontally.

162. The black knight spells out PORTUGAL. The white knight spells BARBADOS.

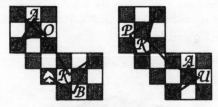

163. LIGHT is the uncircled word.

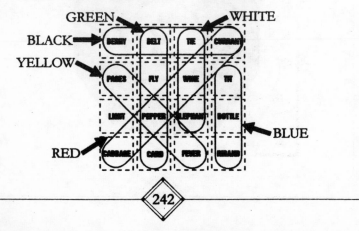

ANSWERS

164. Mathematicians say that "A diameter of a circle subtends a right angle on the circumference". To put this into plain English, imagine a circular pool table. If you strike a ball from the cushion, it will always make a right angle then hit the cushion on the very opposite of the start position:

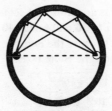

Therefore the way to find one diameter of the circle is to place the right-angle on the circumference and mark the points (A and B) where the set-square cuts the circumference. Draw a straight line between these two. Repeat the whole process. The intersection of the two lines will give you the circle's centre.

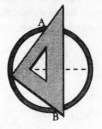

165.

166. The men ran halfway into the tunnel then turned back. The guard would see them approaching and think they were visitors. The soldiers pretended they were visitors but, because they had no paperwork, the guard would "send them back" on their way!

167. The correct route is an arithmetic sequence of 4, 8, 12, 16, 20, 24, 28, 32, skip over to 36 and finally 40. The contestant should choose prize 4, because the number was used in the sequence, not to mention the route taken!

168. Any slice through the upper black dot would cut pizzas 1 to 4 into equal areas. Likewise for any slice through the lower dot for pizzas 5 and 6. Hence slice through the dots:

169. They match up as follows : A & 3, B & 2, C & 1.

170. Call your die A and Mandy's dice B and C. We need A, B and C to be different if we are to stand a chance of winning. The probability that A is not equal to B is 9/10 and the probability that A is not equal to B nor C is 9/10 multiplied by 8/10 (i.e. 72%). So there is a 72% chance that A, B and C are all different. Because any die is equally likely to be the middle value, we divide by three to get the answer of 24%.

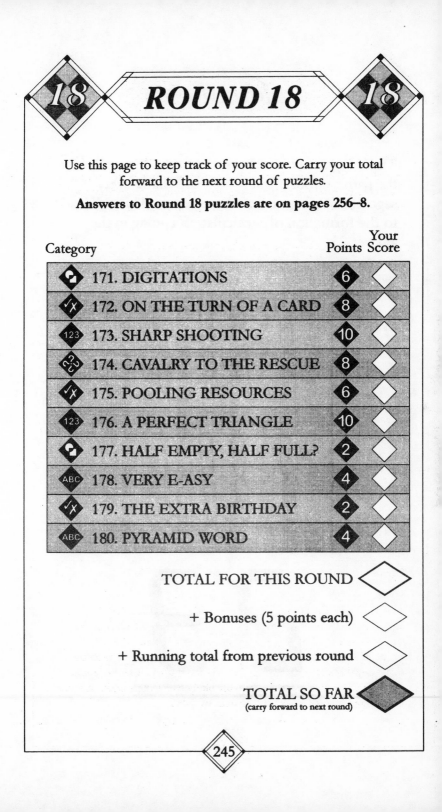

Use this page to keep track of your score. Carry your total forward to the next round of puzzles.

Answers to Round 18 puzzles are on pages 256–8.

Category	Points	Your Score
171. DIGITATIONS	6	
172. ON THE TURN OF A CARD	8	
173. SHARP SHOOTING	10	
174. CAVALRY TO THE RESCUE	8	
175. POOLING RESOURCES	6	
176. A PERFECT TRIANGLE	10	
177. HALF EMPTY, HALF FULL?	2	
178. VERY E-ASY	4	
179. THE EXTRA BIRTHDAY	2	
180. PYRAMID WORD	4	

TOTAL FOR THIS ROUND

+ Bonuses (5 points each)

+ Running total from previous round

TOTAL SO FAR
(carry forward to next round)

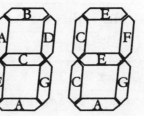

These segments each have a letter on them. To win the game, choose four letters and shade every segment bearing one of those letters. This will lead to the formation of a calculation ending in the answer 23.

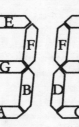

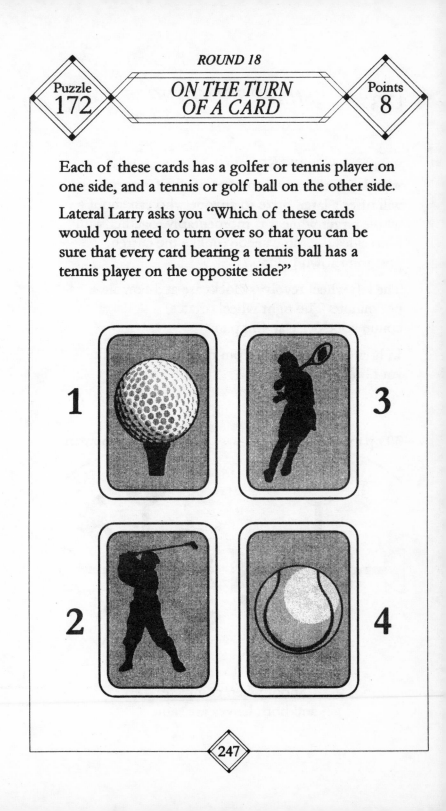

ON THE TURN
OF A CARD

Each of these cards has a golfer or tennis player on one side, and a tennis or golf ball on the other side.

Lateral Larry asks you "Which of these cards would you need to turn over so that you can be sure that every card bearing a tennis ball has a tennis player on the opposite side?"

1

3

2

4

Sideshow Sid's Shooting Stall has a couple of wheels which have a number of "half targets". Sid will offer a large prize to anyone who can shoot a whole target while it is momentarily together with both sides the same shade (unlike the current position shown below).

The left wheel revolves clockwise at 30 revolutions per minute. The right wheel rotates counterclockwise at 45 r.p.m.

In how many seconds from now should you fire your bullet?

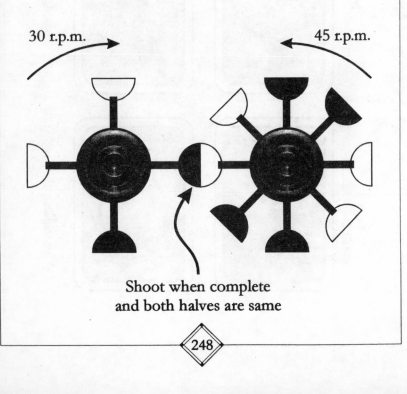

30 r.p.m.

45 r.p.m.

Shoot when complete
and both halves are same

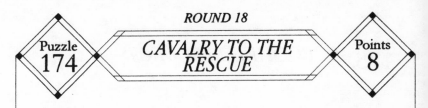

Lateral Larry has another one of his devious chess puzzles waiting for you. "It doesn't look good for White, does it? If it were Black's turn to play next, his Queen can take the White Bishop and it's checkmate.

"Luckily, it's White's turn. How can he win on his next move?"

An attendant is adding chlorine to the brand-new swimming pool that has been built. She has an accurate measuring device which displays the concentration of chlorine in the water. Currently it reads zero.

The label on the packaging says that one pint of chlorine solution must be used for every 500 pints of water. Unfortunately, she has no idea of the pool's dimensions nor how much water is in the pool.

No matter, since the attendant was able to use the exact amount of chlorine without measuring the pool. Furthermore, she only needed one concentration measurement. How did she do it?

A PERFECT TRIANGLE

"This triangle is very special," explains Mandy Math. "The three sides and the perpendicular are four consecutive whole numbers, and there is only one number for which this happens.

"To win the game you must tell me what value x is. As this is a difficult puzzle, I'll give you a free hint. All the numbers are less than 20, and you can try performing Pythagoras' Theorem on the left-hand triangle."

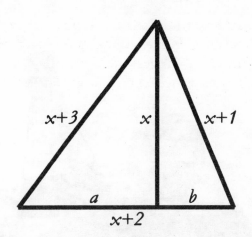

(drawn to scale)

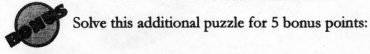 Solve this additional puzzle for 5 bonus points:

Find another method to solve the above puzzle.

"You know the old adage about pessimists and optimists," muses Visual Vern. "Optimists look at a bottle and say that it is half full. Pessimists say that it is half empty.

"Well, here's a bottle. Using nothing more than your hands, tell me precisely whether it is over or under half full."

How can you perform this feat without using any measuring equipment?

Puzzle 178

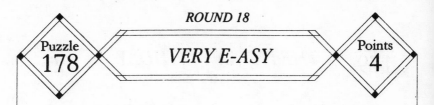

VERY E-ASY

Points 4

Wordsmith Will is hard at work in the Verbal Vault with his new word game.

"This puzzle is one of my 'ee'-siest yet!" he proclaims. "For each row and column, choose the consonants in order so that they fill the blanks to form a word. No consonant is used more than once.

"What are the 14 words?"

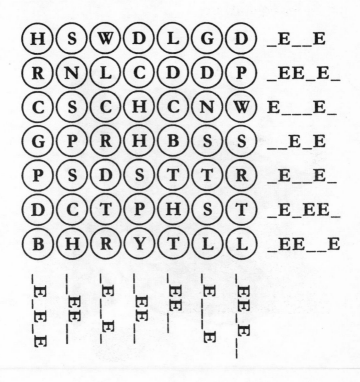

H	S	W	D	L	G	D	_E__E
R	N	L	C	D	D	P	_EE_E_
C	S	C	H	C	N	W	E___E_
G	P	R	H	B	S	S	__E_E
P	S	D	S	T	T	R	_E__E_
D	C	T	P	H	S	T	_E_EE_
B	H	R	Y	T	L	L	_EE__E
_E_E_E	__EE_	_E__E_	__EE_	_EE_	_E__E	_EE_E_	

Lateral Larry celebrated his birthday. "I was born on 10th September 1963 and so today, on 11th September 1996, I am 33 years old.

"The funny thing is that my mother assures me I've had 34 birthdays. Hey, if you can explain that I'll let you have a slice of my cake!"

Where did the extra birthday come from?

PYRAMID WORD

Find the 15-letter word using the clues to help you.

?-SHIRT

PRINTING MEASURE

FOR EVERY

LET IT BE

SCORE

171. Shade in segments bearing B, D, F and G. By appreciating that most digital numbers use the right-hand segments, you can narrow down the combinations. As it happens, all of the right-hand segments are used in the solution:

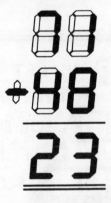

172. Cards 2 and 4. Clearly we need to turn over card 4 to see if there is a tennis player on the other side. We don't care what is on the other side of card 1. Card 2 needs to be turned over because we need to check that, if that had a tennis ball on the hidden side, the statement would be false. Card 3 doesn't need to be turned over – the statement in question does not require every tennis player to have a particular ball on the other side.

173. Never! In half a second, the left-hand wheel turns a quarter of a circle, while the right-hand wheel turns three-eighths of a circle. Numbering the halves every half a second proves that no two halves of the same shade ever meet:

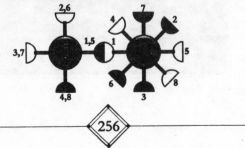

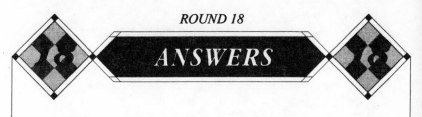

174. White can advance his Pawn to the eighth rank. He could promote this to a Queen, but that doesn't put Black's King in check. As a result, Black still threatens checkmate by taking White's Bishop.

The correct solution is to promote the Pawn and opt to exchange it for a Knight. This puts Black's King in check and, because the Rook and Bishop cover all the squares it could escape to (see diagram), it is also checkmate.

175. Suppose the attendant puts in a tenth of a pint into the pool. After allowing the chlorine to disperse evenly, she takes a reading. Let's say the reading shows a concentration of 0.01%. As the desired concentration is 1 part chlorine to 500 parts water (i.e. 0.2%) she now knows she must add a further 19 tenths of a pint (i.e. 1.9 pints) to reach the correct concentration.

176. Because the diagram is to scale, the easy way to solve this is to measure the lengths of x and $x+1$. Suppose the x side measures 1.8 inches and the $x+1$ side measures 1.95 inches. This means that 1 unit represents a length on paper of 0.15 inches. As x is 1.8 inches long, x can be calculated as $1.8/0.15 = 12$.

A more difficult way to solve this is to use Pythagoras' Theorem which states that for a right-angled triangle with sides a, b and hypotenuse c, then $a^2 = b^2 + c^2$.

(176 contd.)

Performing this on the left-hand triangle we get:

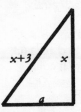

$$(x+3)^2 = x^2 + a^2$$
$$x^2 + 6x + 9 = x^2 + a^2$$
$$3(2x+3) = a^2$$
$\therefore 2x + 3$ has a factor of 3
$\therefore 2x$ must also have a factor of 3
$\therefore x$ must also have a factor of 3

Trying values of 3, 6, 9... for x we find that x must equal 12 because only then does $3(2x+3)$ equal a square number (81).

If you had a protractor, you could also solve the problem by measuring angles and using trigonometry.

177. When a bottle is half full, it is also half empty. Place one thumb over the top of the bottle and the other at the current water level. Then turn the bottle upside-down. If the water level is now above your thumb, the bottle is over half full.

178. Words across (use black circles):
HEDGE, NEEDED, ESCHEW,
GREBE, PESTER, TEPEES, BEETLE.

Words down (use white circles):
RECEDE, SPEECH, WELDER,
CHEESY, LEECH, NESTLE,
DEEPEST.

179. A birthday is defined as "the day on which one is born or its anniversary" (*Chambers English Dictionary*) so Larry has indeed had 34 birthdays.

180. The word formed is T-EM-PER-AMEN-TALLY.

ROUND 19

Use this page to keep track of your score. Carry your total
forward to the next round of puzzles.

Answers to Round 19 puzzles are on pages 270–2.

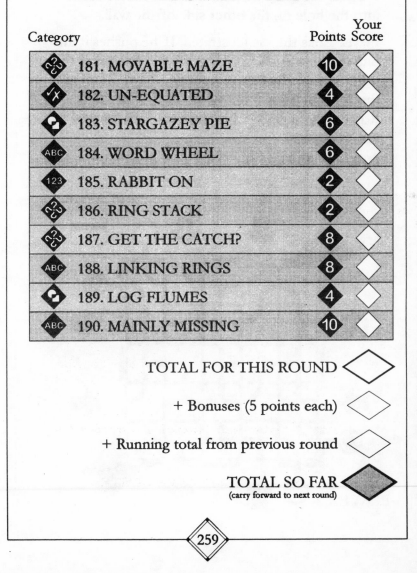

Category		Points	Your Score
	181. MOVABLE MAZE	10	◇
	182. UN-EQUATED	4	◇
	183. STARGAZEY PIE	6	◇
	184. WORD WHEEL	6	◇
	185. RABBIT ON	2	◇
	186. RING STACK	2	◇
	187. GET THE CATCH?	8	◇
	188. LINKING RINGS	8	◇
	189. LOG FLUMES	4	◇
	190. MAINLY MISSING	10	◇

TOTAL FOR THIS ROUND ◇

+ Bonuses (5 points each) ◇

+ Running total from previous round ◇

TOTAL SO FAR ◆
(carry forward to next round)

This game is for two players who sit on either side of a wall. The aim is for each player to make a route in the maze so that their ball can be rolled into the hole on the other side of the wall.

Player 1 has the tile illustrated. If he pushes it into one of holes A, B, C or D a tile will fall out at the other end of the row or column. Player 2 can use this tile and place it in one of E, F, G or H. Rotating a tile before placing back into the grid is not necessary.

How can they win the game with these two moves?

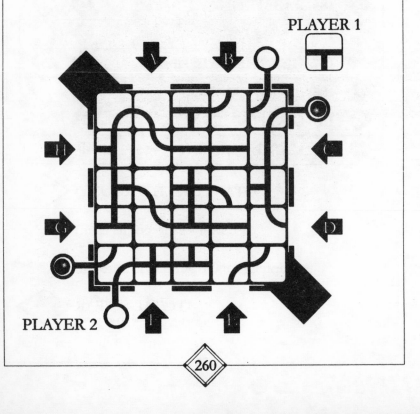

UN-EQUATED

Two people are near the Equator of the Earth.

One of them is experiencing very dry, still and sweltering hot weather.

The other is in an area of damp, very windy and bitterly cold conditions.

How can there be a relatively short distance between the two?

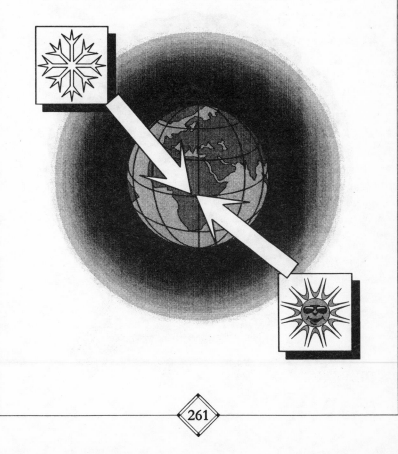

Baker Bill has made a Stargazey Pie, a traditional dish from a region of England.

How can he cut up the pie using six straight cuts of the knife so that each of the four pieces thus formed contain one of the stars? Each piece must be the same shape and size.

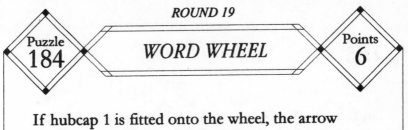

WORD WHEEL

If hubcap 1 is fitted onto the wheel, the arrow spells out the name of a fashion accessory whereas hubcap 2 would imply "following".

What letters are on the tyre?

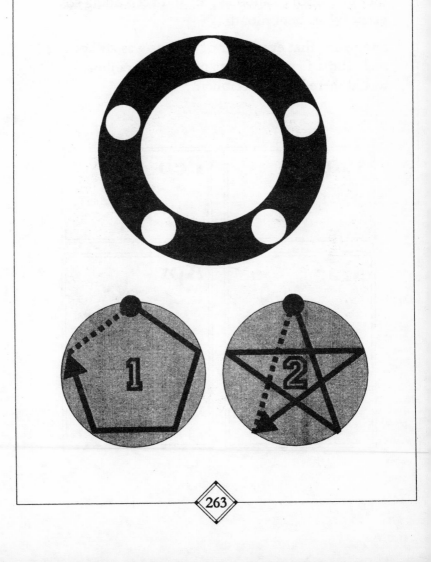

In January this year, a pair of newly born rabbits (a male and female) were introduced into the fairground's Animals Corner.

When any pair of rabbits reach two months old, they give birth to another pair and keep doing so every subsequent month.

Supposing that every pair of rabbits was always a male and a female, how many pairs of rabbits would there be in December?

RING STACK

You catch sight of a beautiful bangle on the arm of Mystic Molly.

"Oh, that's one of my nicest accessories," she says. "It's made from five different materials – ebony, jade, onyx, mother-of-pearl and agate. I love it so much I have another four at home which are identical to this one.

"Here's a little question for you – how can I stack up the five bracelets in a column so that no part of any material is above an identical section of the same type?"

 Solve this additional puzzle for 5 bonus points:

It is only possible to do this with x rings containing x materials when x is ...?

"Take a look at this rope," says Visual Vern. "Can you see the two nails in the middle? Take one of them out so that I can free the rope."

You do so. Vern picks up the spiral's two outermost ropes and pulls them sideways. The rope catches on the nail. "Too bad, you lose," he says.

He replaces the nail and gives you another turn. And another. And another. He always pulls two outermost ropes from the left-hand side but no matter which nail you pick, the rope never slides free.

How does the scam work?

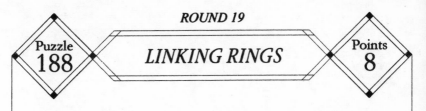

Puzzle 188

LINKING RINGS

Points 8

Each ring spells out a 6-letter word. Each letter fits into one of the circles on the boundary of the intersection in which that letter lives. (For example, the middle 'T' will be in one of the three central circles.)

Using the clues provided, deduce what the words are.

Clues:
Black ring = Performer
Shaded ring = Mimic
White ring = Thin fibre

LOG FLUMES

The carnival owner is designing a new log flume ride. Because the ride is so popular, people can get on at A and ride to B, or get on at B and ride to A.

The owner wishes to design the ride so that either route is equally popular by making them the same distance.

Remove enough pipes so that two separate routes are formed.

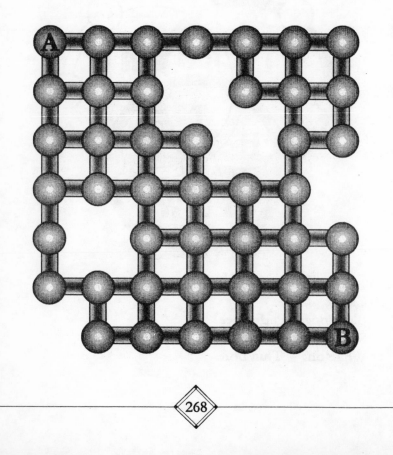

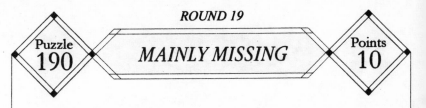

Puzzle
190

MAINLY MISSING

Points
10

"I've just devised a truly devious crossword," boasts Wordsmith Will. "None of the words have clues, and most of the letters are missing.

"OK, so how are you supposed to solve this? Well, the missing letters are either A, E, I, N, R, S, or T and each one is represented by a number. So if you think T=1, replace every 1 by a T.

"Well, what are you waiting for? Fill the puzzle in!"

1	2	3	4	5	6	7
2	■	1	■	6	■	1
3	1	7	6	4	5	3
7	■	M	■	U	■	5
5	M	P	7	1	3	4
6	■	L	■	2	■	7
4	3	2	7	1	5	6

A E I N R S T

181. Player 1 puts the spare piece into B (left diagram). A 90 degree curve falls out, which Player 2 puts into G (right diagram). This forms two separate tracks:

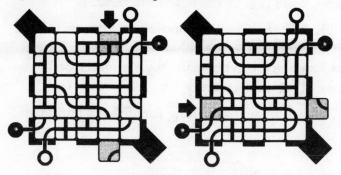

182. The hot person is near the Equator but on the ground. The other person is flying above the Equator, where it is often bitterly cold.

183. The trick is to try this puzzle with a square first. Then, because a circle has at least the same amount of symmetry as a square, one can transfer the solution across:

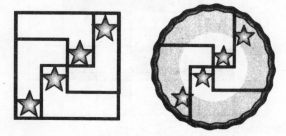

184. Following the path of the arrow, you can spell out BEADS and BASED.

185. This is a very old puzzle which was first set by Leonardo da Vinci. The sequence formed is the well-known Fibonacci Series, where the next term in the series can be calculated using the previous two terms:

Jan	Feb	Mar	Apr	May	Jun	Jul	Aug	Sep	Oct	Nov
1	1	2	3	5	8	13	21	34	55	89

Hence there will be 55 + 89 = 144 rabbit pairs in December.

186. Move each bangle three positions clockwise each time (or counterclockwise each time). Bonus question: This can be done for any *x* which is a prime number.

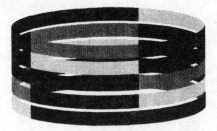

187. The pair of outermost ropes he picks determines whether the white or black nail is caught:

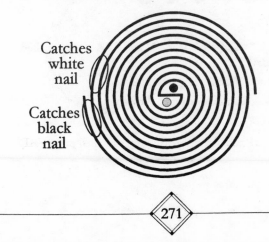

Catches white nail

Catches black nail

188. The words are ARTIST, THREAD and SHADOW:

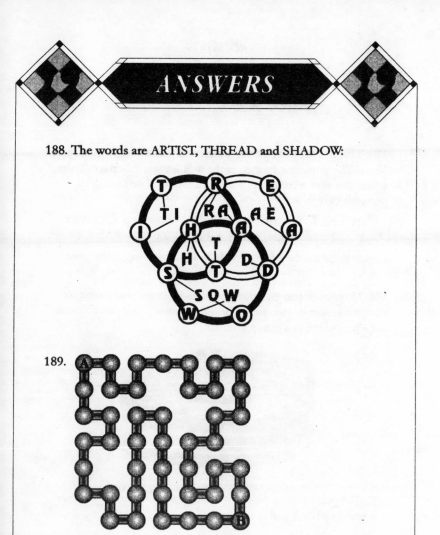

189.

190. 1=R, 2=E, 3=T, 4=S, 5=I, 6=N and 7=A – the finished crossword reads:

ACROSS: Retsina, Transit, Imparts, Stearin

DOWN: Retains, Trample, Insurer, Artisan

ROUND 20

Use this page to keep track of your score. Carry your total forward to the next round of puzzles.

Answers to Round 20 puzzles are on pages 284–6.

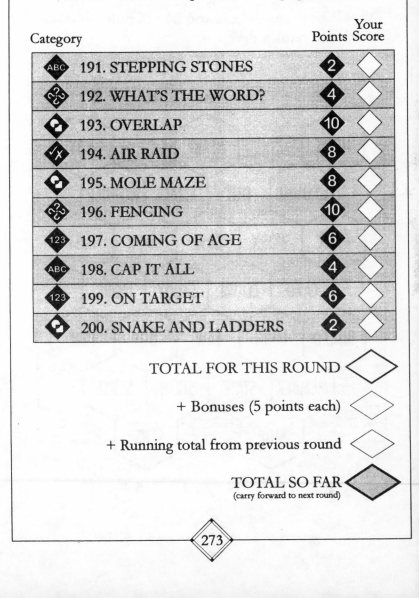

Category	Points	Your Score
191. STEPPING STONES	2	◇
192. WHAT'S THE WORD?	4	◇
193. OVERLAP	10	◇
194. AIR RAID	8	◇
195. MOLE MAZE	8	◇
196. FENCING	10	◇
197. COMING OF AGE	6	◇
198. CAP IT ALL	4	◇
199. ON TARGET	6	◇
200. SNAKE AND LADDERS	2	◇

TOTAL FOR THIS ROUND ◇

+ Bonuses (5 points each) ◇

+ Running total from previous round ◇

TOTAL SO FAR ◆
(carry forward to next round)

Visitors to the carnival can only leave by using the
stepping stones to reach the exit. However, some
of the stones are loose.

What logical route would you take in order to reach
Finish and remain dry?

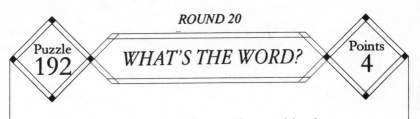

WHAT'S THE WORD?

Mystic Molly has placed a magic word in the bottom of the square cells. However, the cells are so deep that it is only possible to see parts of the letters.

Despite this, can you work out Molly's magic word?

"Here's a straightforward puzzle ... for a change!" says Mandy Math.

"All you have to do is place the four tiles in the box so that four sums are formed and the four answers to these sums are four consecutive numbers (such as 12, 13, 14 and 15).

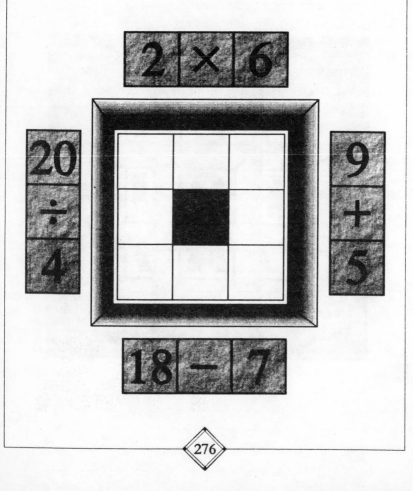

AIR RAID

"The war story I like best," reminisces Lateral Larry, "is that of a brave pilot who was carrying a $2,000,000 cargo in used notes, plundered from enemy banks.

"However, he had not reckoned on an enemy soldier hiding in the cargo bay, who attacked and disarmed him during the middle of the flight home. Fortunately, the assailant couldn't fly and so he had to keep the pilot alive, to fly him where he wanted to land.

"There were only two parachutes in the plane. One on the pilot's back, the other in the co-pilot's seat. The enemy soldier went into the back to examine the money. The pilot saw his chance and disabled *both* parachutes so that they would fail when opened. When the enemy returned the pilot announced that their fuel was running out and they would have to bail out.

"And that pilot was my father who is still alive today, unlike the enemy soldier."

How do you think
the story ended?

One of the attractions at the funfair is the mole maze which consists of a network of tunnels underground, and a network of pathways above ground.

The children start at S, walk to one of the square holes, crawl underground, and emerge out of one of the round holes. They then walk to the next square hole and so on until they reach F.

How should the carnival owner fence the grid so that the children are forced to cover every square, and the length of every overground section is the same? Every hole is used once and only once.

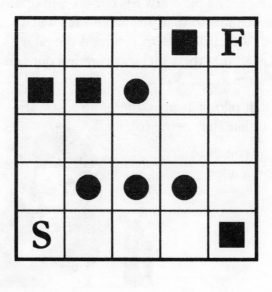

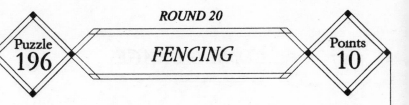

FENCING

Colin the Clown is painting some fence posts of square cross-section. He has already covered the bottom stages with lots of gooey red paint (on the left post) and yellow paint (on the right post) as shown in picture 1.

He leaves the posts to dry but before they do so a changeable wind approaches and blows the posts over, as shown in picture 2. The wind changes direction and blows the posts over the other direction, as in picture 3.

The wind changes three more times. What would the two touching faces of the posts look like when Colin separates them?

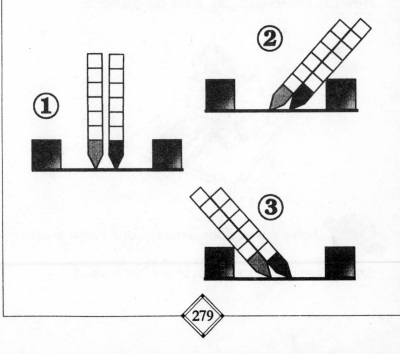

Two of the carnival's circus performers were trying to work out how long they had been working there.

"Well let me see," says one. "On my 37th anniversary with the carnival, my son was in his 11th year here."

"OK," says the other, "well how long has your son been here now?"

"I'm sure I've been here twice as long as he has," says the first man as he scratches his head, desperately trying to remember the exact year.

Meanwhile the second man draws a diagram on a piece of paper. "Solved it!", he exclaims.

How did the second man solve the problem?

 Solve this additional puzzle for 5 bonus points:

Attempt the puzzle above but by another method.

CAP IT ALL

To win the game, decide which letter of the alphabet can be capped onto the start of all these words.

What 9-letter adjective, that perhaps describes certain types of spiders, can be made from these first letters?

ATHLETIC
ATTRACTIVE
HASTENING
MOTIONLESS
REASONABLE
IRRITABLENESS
EVOLUTIONARY
NIGHTFALL
ENCEFORWARD

ON TARGET

In an archery contest, each competitor is given three arrows.

One of the archers aims for the target and fires her first shot. Her subsequent shot is further out from the midpoint of the target (known as the "gold") than her first.

Assuming the arrows land randomly anywhere on the target, what is the probability that her third shot is further from the gold than her first?

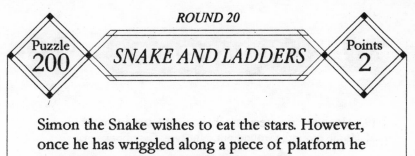

Simon the Snake wishes to eat the stars. However, once he has wriggled along a piece of platform he may not travel over it again. Also, there is not enough room for him to turn around.

What is the largest number of stars he can eat? (And yes, he knows how to climb ladders.)

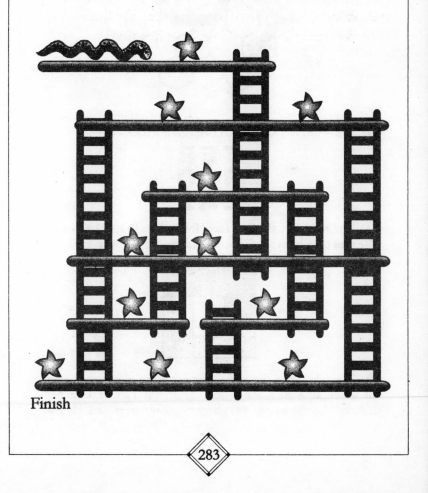

Finish

191. Using word association, the correct route follows the logic of Home ground, Ground nut, Nut case, Case book, etc.:

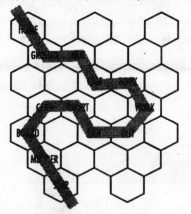

192. The word is TREASURE (read counterclockwise):

193. The results of the four sums formed are 9, 10, 11 and 12. The tiles have been shaded in the diagram to aid the eye:

194. The pilot knew the soldier was not going to jump out over the sea because the money would absorb water and sink. So he deduced that the enemy was going to bail out over land. He also

figured that, although he could have been taken hostage, it was much more likely that the two parachutes were going to be used for the soldier and the money ($2,000,000 would have been too heavy and bulky for the enemy soldier to hold on to). The faulty parachute killed the enemy soldier, but once he had gone the pilot could fly to safety.

195.

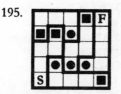

196. Imagine that these diagrams show the state of the touching faces of the posts. The paint transfers between the faces as shown and the diagram on the right is the final answer:

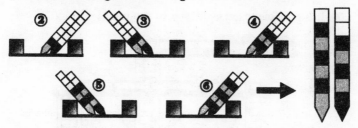

197. The following graph shows that the man has been at the circus for 52 years and his son has been there for 26 years:

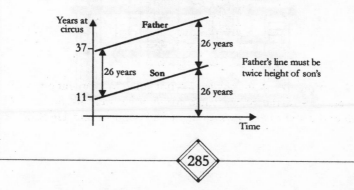

Alternatively, you can use algebra:

$$2 \times (11 + a) = (37 + a)$$
$$22 + 2a = 37 + a$$
$$a = 15$$

Hence $(11 + a) = 26$ and $(37 + a) = 52$.

198. The new words are (A)PATHETIC, (S)ELECTIVE, (C)HASTENING, (E)MOTIONLESS, (T)REASONABLE, (L)IMITABLENESS, (R)EVOLUTIONARY, (I)DENTIFICATION, (W)HENCEFORWARD. The letters in brackets can be rearranged to make CRAWLIEST.

199. Two-thirds, or 2-in-3. The chance that the third arrow will be the best one is one-third. Hence, the probability that it is not the best arrow is one less one-third.

200. It is possible to get every star except one:

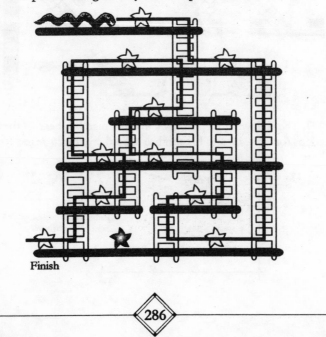

Finish

TEST YOUR STRENGTH

How are you doing? Calculate your score so far and
see how high you can try...

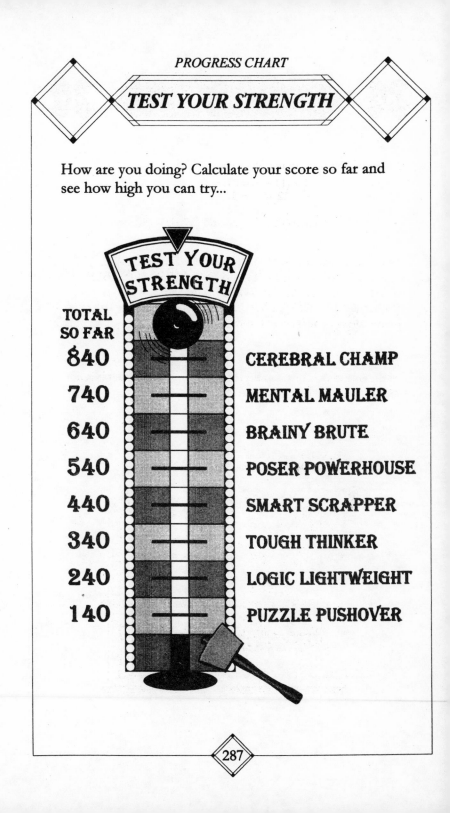

TOTAL SO FAR	
840	CEREBRAL CHAMP
740	MENTAL MAULER
640	BRAINY BRUTE
540	POSER POWERHOUSE
440	SMART SCRAPPER
340	TOUGH THINKER
240	LOGIC LIGHTWEIGHT
140	PUZZLE PUSHOVER

ROUND 21

Use this page to keep track of your score. Carry your total forward to the next round of puzzles.

Answers to Round 21 puzzles are on pages 300–2.

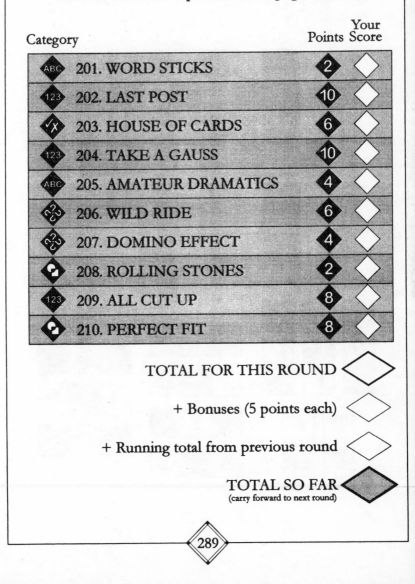

Category	Points	Your Score
201. WORD STICKS	2	◇
202. LAST POST	10	◇
203. HOUSE OF CARDS	6	◇
204. TAKE A GAUSS	10	◇
205. AMATEUR DRAMATICS	4	◇
206. WILD RIDE	6	◇
207. DOMINO EFFECT	4	◇
208. ROLLING STONES	2	◇
209. ALL CUT UP	8	◇
210. PERFECT FIT	8	◇

TOTAL FOR THIS ROUND ◇

+ Bonuses (5 points each) ◇

+ Running total from previous round ◇

TOTAL SO FAR ◆
(carry forward to next round)

To win the game, place the 3-letter tiles onto what remains of this chessboard so that a crossword is formed.

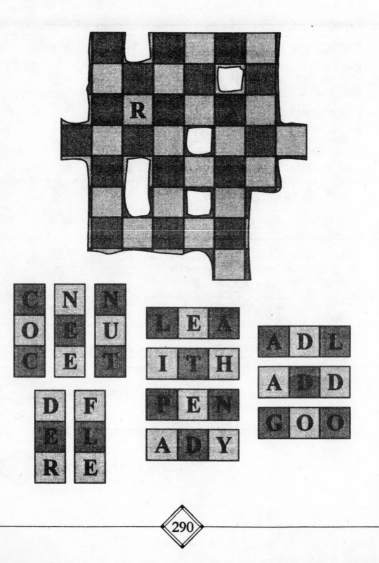

LAST POST

Every day, each household in a particular street expects one letter.

Mike the Mailman delivers the letters to the street. Unfortunately, he does so randomly. Naturally, a number of letters get delivered to the wrong houses and the residents swap letters after Mike has gone.

Over an average year, how many letters per day will Mike deliver correctly?

Mystic Molly begins her story. "In the House of Cards, six playing cards have an argument and wish to separate out into their own suits.

"The King and Queen refuse to have any card of a lower denomination placed on top of them at any time.

"How many moves will it take before the red cards are all in one pile on the left and the black cards are in a pile on the right? Cards of either suit may be put back onto the House of Cards if it is empty, but the rule regarding seniority still applies."

House
of
Cards

| ♥ only | ♥ only | ♣ only | ♣ only |

TAKE A GAUSS

"Here's a history lesson for you," says Mandy Math.

"When he was at school, the German mathematics prodigy Carl Friedrich Gauss discovered that a quick way of adding up the numbers from 1 to 1000 was to consider it as 500 pairs of 1001:

$$1 + 2 + 3 + ... + 998 + 999 + 1000$$

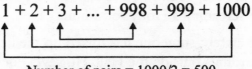

Number of pairs = 1000/2 = 500
Total for series = 500 x 1001 = 500500

"You can take this further. For example, the following series has a starting number of 2, a difference of 3 between consecutive terms, and there are 100 terms in the series:

$$2 + 5 + 8 + ... + 293 + 296 + 299$$

Number of pairs = 100/2 = 50
Total for series = 50 x 301 = 15050

"I know a particular arithmetic series. Its total is 69550, there are 100 terms in it, and the starting number is four times larger than the difference between any two consecutive terms.

"What is the fifth number in the series?"

The carnival is situated on the outside of a small town which has a Civic Hall. Throughout the winter, the amateur dramatics group will be performing a dramatization of a famous book and staging a musical to keep the citizens amused during the fairground's quiet season. The Hall will also be screening a Hollywood film.

Unfortunately, someone has mixed up the letters on the hoardings outside the Hall. However, luckily they possibly give a better description than the real titles!

Can you work out the famous titles?

Book
(6,2,4)

Musical
(1,1,1,8)

Film
(3,7,2,3,5)

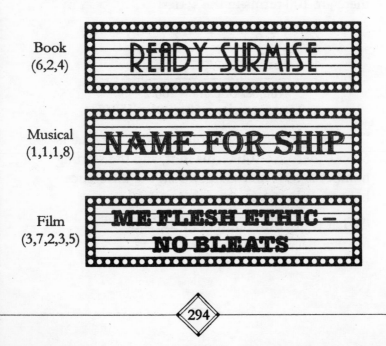

READY SURMISE

NAME FOR SHIP

ME FLESH ETHIC – NO BLEATS

WILD RIDE

One of the carnival's scariest rides, The Bullet, is a steep, U-shaped 100 yard rollercoaster with a straight track.

Riders lie down in their carriage and are propelled feet first down the steep slope. When they reach the bottom, the carriage is hauled up the other side of the "U" so that they can get off and allow the next group their moment of terror.

The coaster is so terrifying that riders' heads move 101 yards whereas their feet move 99 yards, and yet they remain in perfectly good health.

Can you explain how?

How can these 5-letter domino tiles be arranged between the cubes below so that five related words are formed?

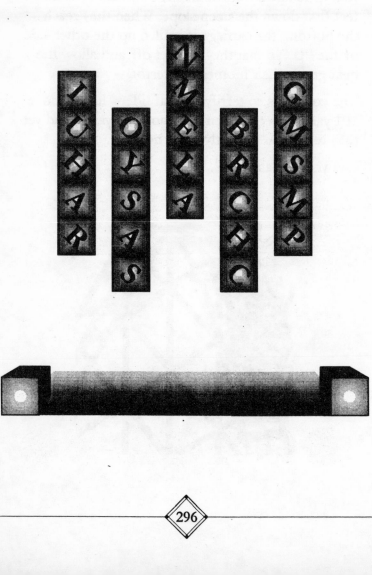

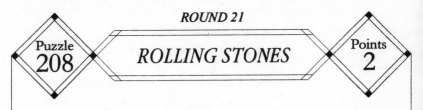

ROLLING STONES

Pick a boulder and place it on one of the numbered circles. Then roll it straight along one line into another empty space.

Do the same for the remaining six boulders.

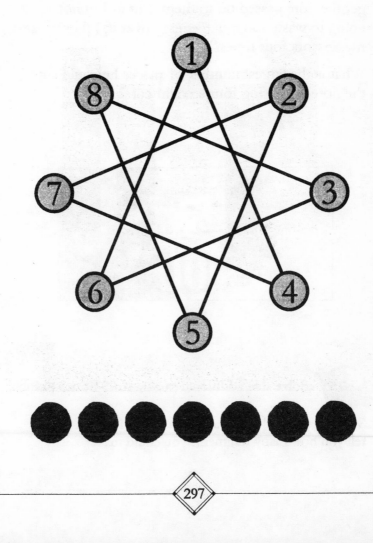

Sideshow Sid is furious. "Someone has paid for a go on my stall using a foreign note and I didn't realize," he complains.

"I'm so mad I'm going to cut up the note using my pair of trustworthy scissors so that no one else will get the note passed on to them. But as I'm not going to waste too much energy over it, I'll only use my scissors four times."

What is the largest number of pieces he could cut the note into using four straight cuts?

 Solve this additional puzzle for 5 bonus points:

Suppose you had *n* cuts available. What formula would tell you how many fragments you could make?

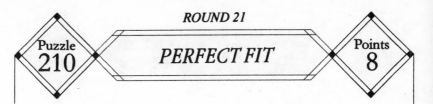

PERFECT FIT

Lateral Larry has 25 pieces left to fill in this (rather boring!) jigsaw.

"I'd rather you fill it in for me," he says. "And you can win some points here if you can find the minimum number of fits necessary to finish the jigsaw. I can see a way of doing it using seven fits."

Read Larry's mind and discover how this can be achieved.

25 of 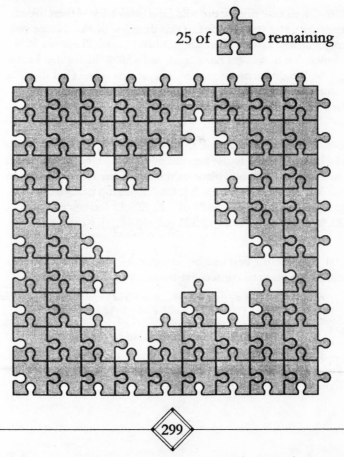 remaining

201.

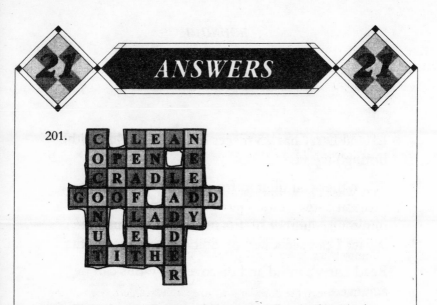

202. Given that you are not told how many houses there are in the street, you can assume that this does not matter. Hence you might as well assume there are just two houses. There is a 50% chance that he will get none right, and a 50% chance that he will get both right, so on average he will get one correct per day. The same calculation can be performed for any other number of houses, but the answer is always one.

203. 14 moves are required. In this solution, Jh-R1 means "move the Jack of Hearts to the first red pile", and Kc-H means "move the King of Clubs and place on the top of the House." Solution: Kh-R1, Kc-B1, Qh-R2, Qc-B2, Kh-R2 (on top of Qh), Kc-B2 (on top of Qc), Jh-R1, Jc-B1, Kh-H, Qh-R1 (on top of Jh), Kh-R1 (red finished), Kc-H, Qc-B1 (on top of Jc), Kc-B1.

204. Suppose the first number in the series was called a and the difference between consecutive terms was d. Then we have:

$$69550 = a + (a+d) + (a+2d) + \ldots + (a+97d) + (a+98d) + (a+99d)$$
$$= 100a + (0+1+2+\ldots+97+98+99)d$$
$$= 100a + (50 \text{ pairs of } 99d)$$
$$= 400d + (50 \times 99)d \quad [\text{since } a=4d \text{ by the question}]$$
$$69550 = 5350d$$

Then $d = 69550 / 5350 = 13$, and hence $a = 52$. So the fifth term of the series is $a + 4d = 104$.

ANSWERS

205. *Murder is Easy* (Agatha Christie), *H.M.S. Pinafore* (Gilbert and Sullivan), *The Silence of the Lambs*.

206. When the carriage reaches the bottom of the U-shape, it is turned around so that it is pointing in the correct direction by the time it is hauled up the opposite side of the slope. The consequence of this is that the riders' heads travel some of the journey twice, hence the difference in distance.

207. Rearrange the domino tiles so that the top letters are in the order B, I, N, G and O. Now topple them, and the names of five games can be read horizontally (namely, BINGO, RUMMY, CHESS, HALMA and CRAPS).

208. Place the first boulder in circle 4, then roll it to 1. Place the second boulder in circle 7 then roll it to 4, so that the second boulder finishes where the second one started from. Continue using this logic (i.e. 2 to 7, 5 to 2, 8 to 5, 3 to 8 and finally 6 to 3). The key to this puzzle is that 3 shares no common factors with 8.

209. Eleven pieces. The best way to ensure the correct number is to mark equidistant numbers along two sides and connect up the numbers with the same total:

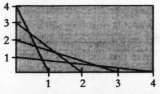

The first cut makes one extra piece. The second cut makes two more, the third cut three more and so on. So the number of new pieces formed is 1, 3, 6, 10, 15, 21... (called the "Triangle Numbers") for 1, 2, 3, 4, 5, 6... cuts respectively. By including an extra one to count the original note, we get 2, 4, 7, 11 etc. The formula for the number of pieces is $\frac{1}{2}n(n+1) + 1$, where n is the number of cuts.

210. Arrange the pieces into five groups of four as shown on the right. Place the first five pieces in the middle to form five crosses. For the sixth "fit", place the outer cross into the middle. The final fit completes the jigsaw.

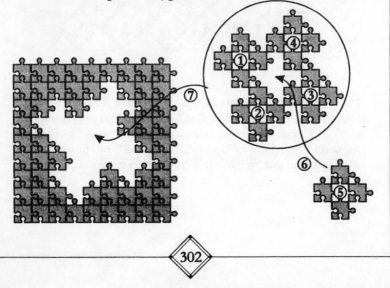

ROUND 22

Use this page to keep track of your score. Carry your total forward to the next round of puzzles.

Answers to Round 22 puzzles are on pages 314–16.

Category	Points	Your Score
211. KEYBOARD QUIZ	8	◇
212. DIZZY BIRD	4	◇
213. CIRCUS CIRCLES	4	◇
214. FUNNELS	8	◇
215. LEAPFROGS	10	◇
216. X MARKS THE SPOT	6	◇
217. SQUARE BASHING	6	◇
218. PROBABLY	2	◇
219. THE CHOCOLATE GAME	10	◇
220. THE LEVITATING EGG	2	◇

TOTAL FOR THIS ROUND ◇

+ Bonuses (5 points each) ◇

+ Running total from previous round ◇

TOTAL SO FAR ◆
(carry forward to next round)

KEYBOARD QUIZ

"This puzzle is difficult but straightforward," explains Wordsmith Will.

"On this keyboard I tried to type a six-letter word which means 'more greasy'.

"By accident, my fingers all slipped one key to the right. To my surprise, I had spelled out another word which means 'partner'. The first letter was on the top row, the second on the second row, the third on the third row, and the final three letters were all on the top row.

"To win the puzzle, tell me which two words were involved."

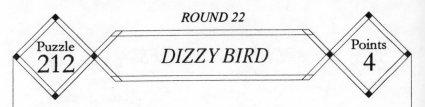

DIZZY BIRD

Patrick the Penguin wants to walk to the South Pole, about 10 miles from where he currently lives.

Because many people (and penguins) have been to the South Pole before, he is going to reach there in a unique way by going in a south-easterly direction until the tip of his beak is over the exact point designated to be the South Pole.

Patrick's penguin friend, Ernie the Emperor, thinks he is mad to try this stunt. Why might he have good reason for doubting Patrick's chances?

CIRCUS CIRCLES

These hoopla rings seem to have been dropped carelessly on the floor. However, in fact there is a hidden logic.

What number should replace the question mark in order to continue the logic?

Puzzle
214

FUNNELS

Points
8

How should you arrange the funnels provided so
that, when the lid is released, the mustard will travel
through all the funnels and onto your hot dog?

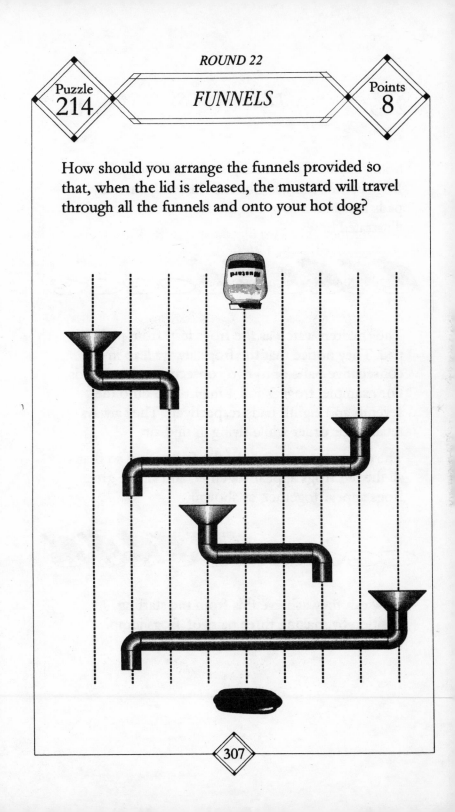

Some children are looking at the red and green frogs in the Animals Corner. Currently their lily pads are all in a row, and the frogs are in the order illustrated here:

The children watch as the frogs leap from pad to pad. They notice that the frogs always leap in consecutive pairs onto two consecutive empty pads. For example, frogs 3 and 4 might leap onto the seventh and eighth pads respectively. They always retain their order while flying in mid-air.

The children want to make the frogs jump so that all the red frogs appear together, and all the green frogs appear together, as shown:

How can they achieve this from the starting position by making three pairs of frogs jump?

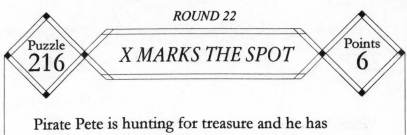

X MARKS THE SPOT

Pirate Pete is hunting for treasure and he has narrowed its location down to one of the Xs in the diagram below. He also knows he needs to connect three pairs of diagrams with a line to discover where to dig.

Under which X is the treasure hidden?

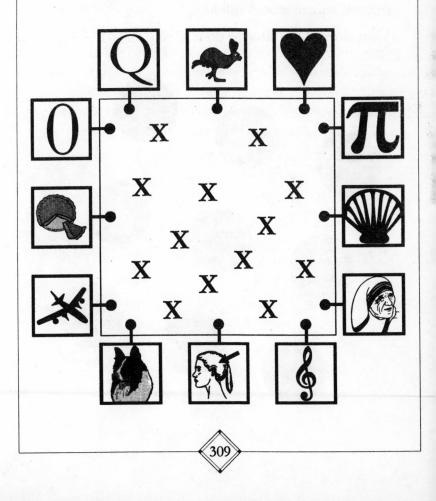

SQUARE BASHING

Visual Vern has a set of nine coins. "I like this arrangement very much. There are eight rows of three coins, including the two main diagonals," he explains.

"However, someone told me that I could slide just four of these coins so that they take up a smaller area on the table and yet the properties of the original square would still hold."

Vern worked out how to do it. Can you?

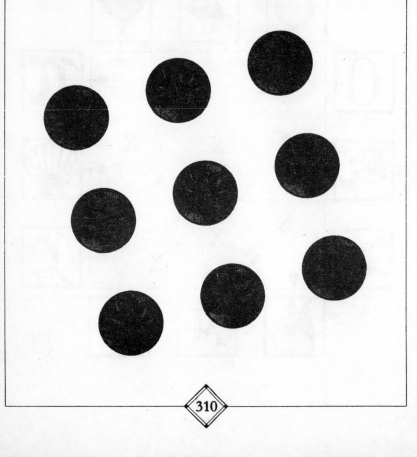

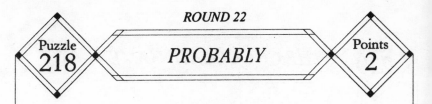

PROBABLY

Mystic Molly has some old coins on a string. Each of the coins has a letter of the alphabet on it, as shown here:

If she turns each coin over, you can see that there are other letters on the reverse sides:

Suppose Molly was to spin the coins on the string so that they stop at random with either face showing. What is the probability that a six-letter word can be read?

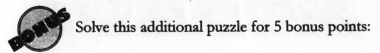 Solve this additional puzzle for 5 bonus points:

I have the letters E, I, P, R, S and T in a bag. If I draw out the letters one at a time, what is the chance that I will spell out a word?

"Here is a bar of chocolate," explains Visual Vern. "We are going to take turns to break the bar straight along any one of the grooves and eat what we break off. For example, if I made a break down the line illustrated, I would have four pieces that I must eat.

"Unfortunately, one of the pieces is poisoned. Whoever is forced to eat that piece loses the game."

Given the choice of going first or second, what is the foolproof strategy to ensure that you are not left with the poisoned piece?

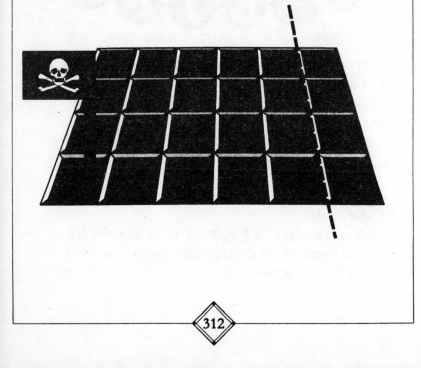

THE LEVITATING EGG

Puzzle
220

Points
2

While you are enjoying your breakfast in the Carnival Café, Marvin the Magician arrives and sits opposite you. "Mind if I join you?" he asks.

He is having a boiled egg. Just before he cracks it open, he says, "What's that outside the window?" You cast your gaze outside but there doesn't seem to be anything there. As you look back at Marvin you see that he has put his egg on the table, his finger keeping it upright.

"Watch this," he says. He blows on the egg and withdraws his finger. Remarkably, the egg stays upright. "Actually, I'm not that hungry. You have the egg," he volunteers as he leaves.

You pick up the egg and find that it is perfectly ordinary, and that neither the egg nor the table has been glued or fixed down in any way.

How did Marvin pull off his trick?

211. I intended to type WAXIER but instead I typed ESCORT.

212. Theoretically, Patrick would continue to circle around the South Pole forever because it is not possible to reach it exactly from a south-easterly direction. He would keep circling the Pole in a smaller and smaller spiral. To explain: suppose he were to do the trip in reverse. At the start he would need to set out in a north-westerly direction. This is not possible because all directions lead north from the South Pole.

213. The circles conform to the following rule:

Therefore the question mark should be replaced with 3, because this circle has three crossover points with the other circles.

214. The funnels are of 2, 3, 6 and 7 units in length. Therefore, the way to structure them is for the 2 and 7 to go in one direction, and the 3 and 6 to go in the other direction so that they cancel each other out.

Because the funnels must be symmetrical, it is permissible to turn two of the funnels around to achieve this. The mirror image of the solution illustrated is also correct.

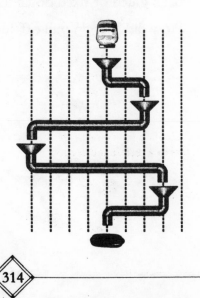

215. The successful sequence of jumps is as follows:

216. Pirate Pete needs to connect the three pairs of homophones – NONE and NUN, HAIR and HARE, and PI and PIE. The X in the triangle formed by the connecting lines is the one where the treasure is buried.

217. Slide the coins as shown below. Notice how the square now tilts in a different direction:

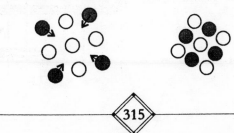

218. The six possible words are BUCKET, CASTLE, BASKET, CASKET, BUSTLE and CACKLE. Each of the six coins has two possible states, so there are $2^6 = 64$ possible positions. Hence the chance is 6-in-64 or, if you prefer, 3-in-32 (about 9%).

For the Bonus question, there are five words possible (ESPRIT, PRIEST, RIPEST, SPRITE and STRIPE) and there are 720 combinations (since $720 = 6 \times 5 \times 4 \times 3 \times 2 \times 1$). So the chance is 5-in-720 or, in simpler terms, 1-in-144.

219. If the chocolate bar is rectangular you play first and cut off the pieces which makes the bar square in shape. On his move, your opponent has no choice but to make the bar "un-square" so that you can square it off again. This tactic works because the final piece is square itself, so all square shapes are safe positions and all rectangular ones are unsafe.

If, at the beginning of the game, you start with a square bar of chocolate, you naturally elect your opponent to go first.

220. Marvin shook some salt onto the table when he distracted you. Tiny grains of salt at the base of the egg would have been enough to keep it upright. He "blew on the egg" to blow away any excess grains of salt.

316

ROUND 23

Use this page to keep track of your score. Carry your total forward to the next round of puzzles.

Answers to Round 23 puzzles are on pages 328–30.

Answers to Round 23 puzzles are on pages 328–30.

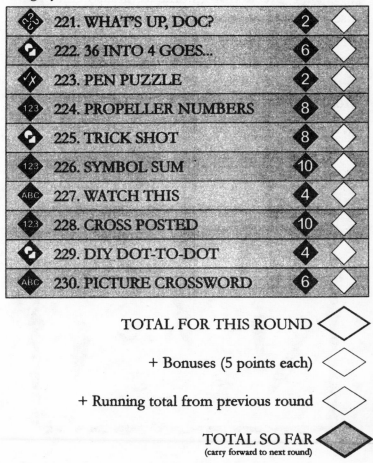

Category	Points	Your Score
221. WHAT'S UP, DOC?	2	◇
222. 36 INTO 4 GOES...	6	◇
223. PEN PUZZLE	2	◇
224. PROPELLER NUMBERS	8	◇
225. TRICK SHOT	8	◇
226. SYMBOL SUM	10	◇
227. WATCH THIS	4	◇
228. CROSS POSTED	10	◇
229. DIY DOT-TO-DOT	4	◇
230. PICTURE CROSSWORD	6	◇

TOTAL FOR THIS ROUND ◇

+ Bonuses (5 points each) ◇

+ Running total from previous round ◇

TOTAL SO FAR ◆
(carry forward to next round)

Farmer Giles is trying to keep Warren the rabbit and his pals from eating the prize carrots.

To achieve this, the farmer wishes to put one fence between the two dots. Naturally, the fence will need to change direction from time to time so Giles will use a number of straight fences and then link them up into one long fence.

All of the rabbits will end up on one side of the fence, and the carrots will be on the other side, safe from the hungry rabbits.

What route should he take? The fence must be made up of no more than thirteen parts.

Puzzle
222

36 INTO 4 GOES...

Points
6

A group of four children are having a campfire and they decide to have some marshmallows. Unfortunately, the marshmallows have got a little warm in their backpack.

Some of the marshmallows are strawberry, some are lemon, and some are blackcurrant – denoted by symbols in the illustration below.

How can they separate out the gooey mess into four pieces of equal size and shape, ensuring that each child's piece includes one strawberry, one lemon and one blackcurrant marshmallow?

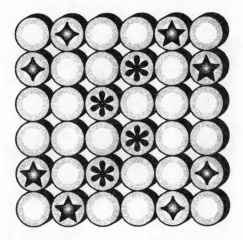

 Solve this additional puzzle for 5 bonus points:

Find a different way of dividing up the marshmallows.

The sheep in the fairground's Animals Corner are causing havoc. The animal warden has three pens at her disposal which she can make into three squares or three rectangles.

How should she pen up the sheep so that the number of sheep in each compartment is odd and less than 4?

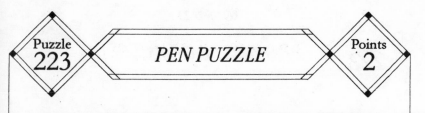 Solve this additional puzzle for 5 bonus points:

Find a completely different solution to the above puzzle.

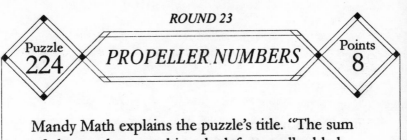

PROPELLER NUMBERS

Mandy Math explains the puzzle's title. "The sum of the numbers touching the left propeller blade equals the sum of the numbers touching the right blade.

"However, the property will not hold for any of the other six possible positions. For example, 4+5 does not equal 11+12, likewise for 6+7 and 13+14.

"Rearrange the numbers so that, no matter where the propeller rests, the property holds true."

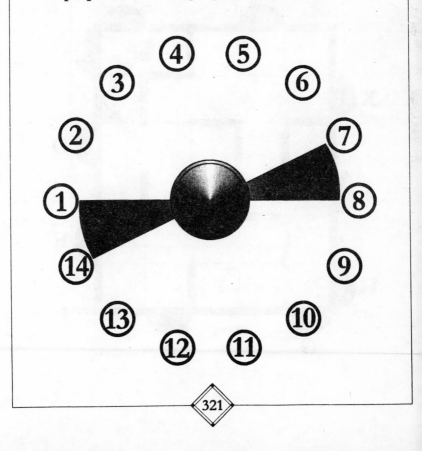

TRICK SHOT

Visual Vern has constructed a table for the carnival's pool hall. Unfortunately, he seems to have been a little over-enthusiastic with the cushions.

He is testing the table out by firing the cue ball in the direction shown. Assuming he has hit the ball hard enough, which pocket will the ball fall into?

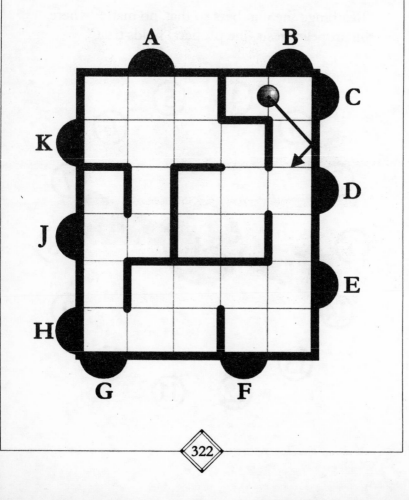

Replace the symbols with numerals so that the
multiplication sum makes sense.

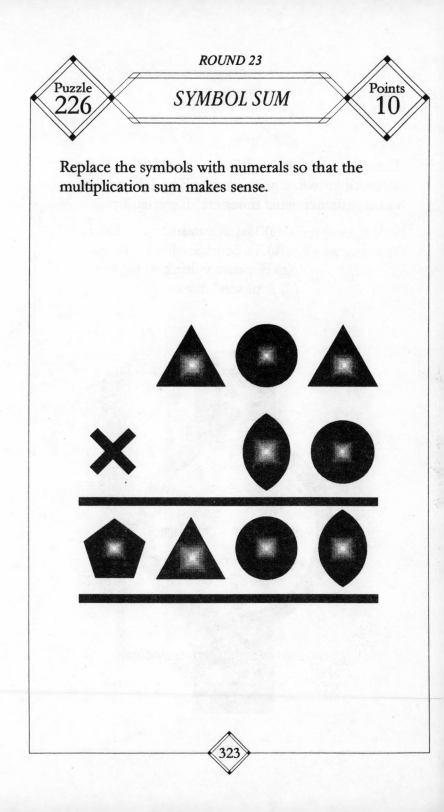

WATCH THIS

If 6:10 is a well-known *Beatles* song, 1:25 is featured in a well-known children's song, and 1:40 implies a good gardener, what times are suggested by:

     (a) Illegal goods
     (b) To be pleased
     (c) Expensive drink
     (d) A pirates' disease?

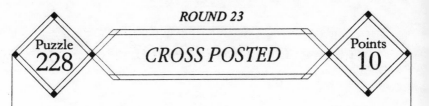

CROSS POSTED

The carnival has two main tents. The larger is 8 yards high, the smaller 6 yards tall. The distance between them is 14 yards.

There are two ropes which are used to steady the tents during high winds. Each rope connects the top of one tent to the bottom of the main post of the other.

What is the horizontal distance, marked *x* on the diagram, between the larger tent's post and the crossover point of the ropes?

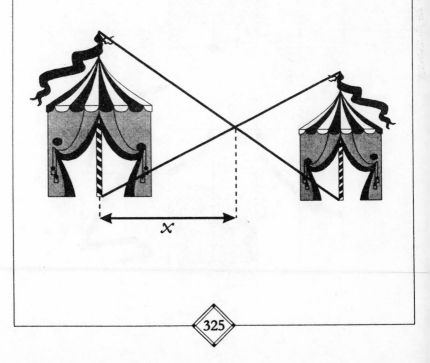

x

Place the curves in the bottom grid between the pairs of dots in the middle grid. When you have placed all the curves, a picture will be formed.

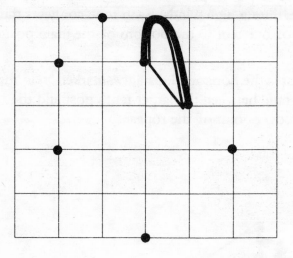

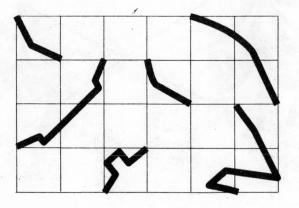

PICTURE CROSSWORD

"Here's a crossword I designed for illiterate people," says Wordsmith Will. "Sadly it was fatally flawed! Each picture represents a word. Once the words are fitted into the grid, the shaded letters can be rearranged to form a word."

221. There are several solutions, and it is possible to do the puzzle regardless of whether you put the rabbits above the fence (as shown in this example) or below it.

222. Two example solutions:

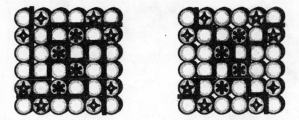

223. To find one solution is easy, but finding the other is more difficult:

224. Notice that if $14 + 1 = 8 + 7$, then $14 - 8 = 7 - 1$. In other words, the difference between pairs of opposite numbers needs to be the same. For this to work for the whole circle, we need all opposite pairs of numbers around the circle to have the same

difference. There are two ways this can be done, with a difference of either 2 or 7 between the numbers. Taking the latter case as an example, we pair up the numbers 1 & 8, 2 & 9, 3 & 10, 4 & 11, 5 & 12, 6 & 13 and 7 & 14 to give us:

225. It will fall into pocket G.

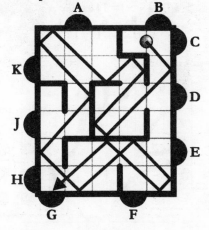

226. The question says "numerals" not "numbers" for good reason. Replacing the circle with I, the leaf shape with V, the triangle with X, the square with L and the pentagon with C, the roman numeral sum XIX times VI equals CXIV (namely, 19 × 6 = 114) is formed.

227. All the clues refer to two-word phrases, whereby the hour hand gives the first word and the minute hand gives the second word. The answers are 4:50 (Black Market), 12:45 (Tickled Pink), 9:15 (Pink Champagne) and 6:35 (Yellow Fever).

228. Because the distance between the tent posts is equal to the sum of the heights, the distance x is the same as the height of the larger tent, i.e. 8 yards. The mathematical argument goes:

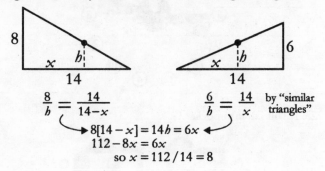

$$\frac{8}{h} = \frac{14}{14-x} \qquad \frac{6}{h} = \frac{14}{x} \quad \text{by "similar triangles"}$$

$$8[14 - x] = 14h = 6x$$
$$112 - 8x = 6x$$
$$\text{so } x = 112/14 = 8$$

229. A coffee-pot is formed:

230. The answers are: 1. Gasmask, 2. Astronaut, 3. Mole, 5. Ostrich, 6. Keyhole, 7. Satellite, 8. Rook, 10. Knee, 11. Chainmail, 12. Steeple. The shaded letters make the word SOLUTION.

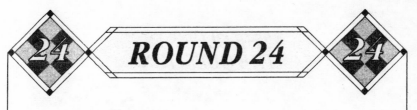

ROUND 24

Use this page to keep track of your score. Carry your total forward to the next round of puzzles.

Answers to Round 24 puzzles are on pages 342–4.

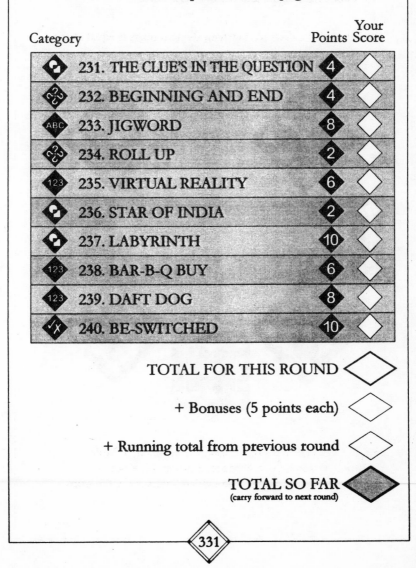

Category		Points	Your Score
	231. THE CLUE'S IN THE QUESTION	4	◇
	232. BEGINNING AND END	4	◇
ABC	233. JIGWORD	8	◇
	234. ROLL UP	2	◇
123	235. VIRTUAL REALITY	6	◇
	236. STAR OF INDIA	2	◇
	237. LABYRINTH	10	◇
123	238. BAR-B-Q BUY	6	◇
123	239. DAFT DOG	8	◇
	240. BE-SWITCHED	10	◇

TOTAL FOR THIS ROUND ◇

+ Bonuses (5 points each) ◇

+ Running total from previous round ◇

TOTAL SO FAR ◆
(carry forward to next round)

How does the sequence below end?

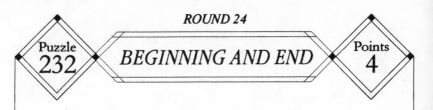

BEGINNING AND END

The nine words below have had two letters removed from their start and finish, the same letters on either end.

Your task is to bring back each word to its former glory. To help you, the letter pairs appear in the grid underneath. Letter pairs appear either horizontally or vertically. Taking the top-left corner as an example, one letter pair must be LY or LM.

What are the nine words?

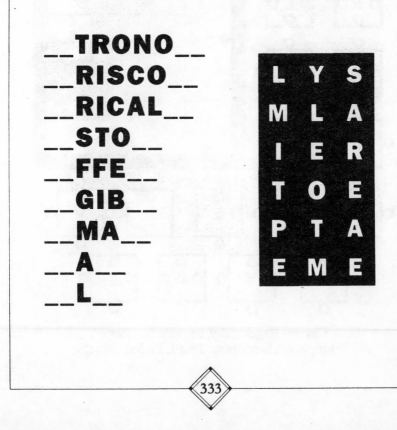

```
__TRONO__
__RISCO__
__RICAL__
__STO__
__FFE__
__GIB__
__MA__
__A__
__L__
```

```
L  Y  S
M  L  A
I  E  R
T  O  E
P  T  A
E  M  E
```

Your aim is to construct a word square. This is done by interlocking the jigsaw pieces into the frame.

Clues to all eight words are given at the bottom of the page, but in random order.

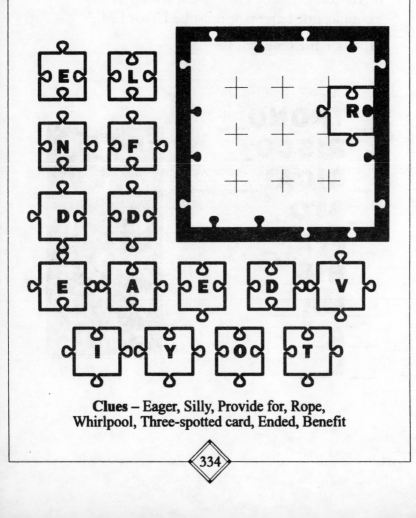

Clues – Eager, Silly, Provide for, Rope, Whirlpool, Three-spotted card, Ended, Benefit

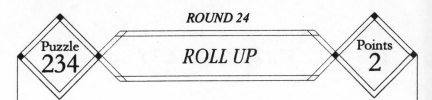

ROLL UP

"Here is one of my gambling dice," says Mandy
Math. "Currently it is standing on the bottom-right
square with its six face uppermost.

"Suppose I rolled it one square left, one square up
and one square right. Draw what the upper face
would look like then."

"I'm a bit hard up at the moment," says a sorrowful Visual Vern. "I needed nine coins to show you my new game but I only have six."

He has a bright idea. "Hang on a minute." He rummages around underneath his stall and reappears with a mirror.

"There are seven coins in this picture. Yes, I know there are only five but at least it looks like seven. There are five lines you can draw which will pass through exactly three coins.

"My challenge to you is this – add the sixth coin so that there are now ten lines of three coins."

MIRROR

Puzzle
236

STAR OF INDIA

Points
2

Which star will enable you to complete the picture of the Taj Mahal?

LABYRINTH

"Here's a straightforward maze for a change," explains Visual Vern. "All you have to do is travel through the labyrinth and pick up all the stars on the way."

What route would you take if you did not want to travel through any part of the maze more than once?

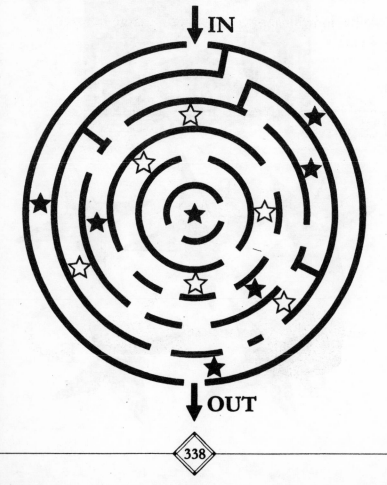

IN

OUT

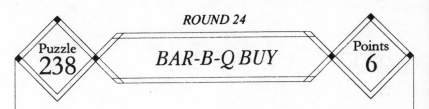

BAR-B-Q BUY

Bob the Butcher is barbecuing again. Each skewer holds two items of food and is priced according to the total for those two items.

He has three hungry customers waiting but unfortunately one wants the hot dog, the second wants the chop and the third likes the look of the burger.

What individual prices should he charge for each item?

Dilbert the Dog is walking around the carnival with his owner, Mr Jones, when he spots Mrs Jones in the distance, walking directly towards them. Dilbert runs off to meet her.

However, as soon as he gets there he immediately turns around and runs back to Mr Jones. He continues to run back and forth between his owners.

Mr and Mrs Jones are currently 300 feet apart. Mr Jones is walking towards Mrs Jones at 3 feet per second; Mrs Jones is walking towards Mr Jones at 2 feet per second. Dilbert runs at a constant speed of 6 feet per second.

When Mr and Mrs Jones eventually meet, what is the total distance that Dilbert has run?

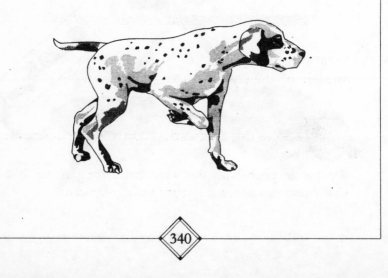

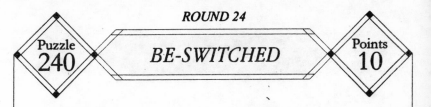

BE-SWITCHED

Lateral Larry has a very complicated lighting system in his house. There are four switches which control the main light. He brings out a card which reminds him of how to use it:

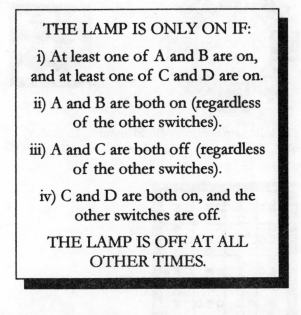

THE LAMP IS ONLY ON IF:

i) At least one of A and B are on, and at least one of C and D are on.

ii) A and B are both on (regardless of the other switches).

iii) A and C are both off (regardless of the other switches).

iv) C and D are both on, and the other switches are off.

THE LAMP IS OFF AT ALL OTHER TIMES.

What is the simplest rule Larry can use to remind himself of the combinations when the lamp is off?

 Solve this additional puzzle for 5 bonus points:

What is the probability that a random setting of the four switches will result in light being provided?

231. The answer is shown on the right. If the picture is reflected in a vertical axis, the work SEQUENCE can be clearly seen. Because the question asked how the "sequence" ends (!) we need a backwards E (shown right) to complete the picture.

232. The words are MEtronoME, PEriscoPE, LYricalLY, REstoRE, TAffeTA, LEgibLE, TOmaTO, MIaMI and SAlSA.

233.

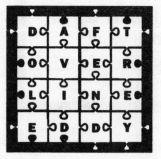

234. Perhaps surprisingly, the six face will still be uppermost, although it will have rotated through 90 degrees:

ANSWERS

235. Place the sixth coin as shown:

236. Star D completes the picture.

237. The pattern of stars goes black, white, black, white...
throughout the maze.

238. You can use algebra to solve the problem, but here's a
simpler way of thinking about it. The total of all three prices is
$4.40. This includes every item twice (because each item is on
two skewers), so the sum of the prices for the burger, chop and
hot dog is half this ($2.20). The chop and burger costs $1.65,
hence the hot dog must cost $2.20 less $1.65 = 55 cents.
Likewise, the burger costs 70 cents ($2.20 – $1.50) and the chop
costs 95 cents ($2.20 – $1.25).

239. Relative to one another, Mr and Mrs Jones are travelling at 5 feet per second. Therefore it will take 300/5 = 60 seconds before the two people meet (using Time equals Distance divided by Speed). Because Dilbert is running at 6 feet per second, he will cover 6 × 60 = 360 feet during this time. (We assume that it takes negligible time for him to turn around.)

240. Treating the lamps in pairs, the following table can be formed:

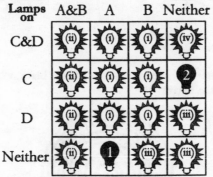

The numbers on the bulbs refer to the clue which dictated that it must be lit.

From this we can see that the simplest rule that Larry can use to remind himself of when the lamp is off is "Only switch A or switch C is on."

As fourteen out of the sixteen possible combinations result in a lit light, the answer to the Bonus is clearly 14-in-16 (or 7-in-8).

ROUND 25

Use this page to keep track of your score. Carry your total forward to the next round of puzzles.

Answers to Round 25 puzzles are on pages 356–8.

Category	Points	Your Score
ABC **241.** SQUARING THE CIRCLES	4	◇
242. CASH AND GRAB	8	◇
243. IN DETAIL	6	◇
244. PICK A PRIZE	10	◇
245. SYMBOLISM	6	◇
ABC **246.** WHEELIES	2	◇
123 **247.** NO MATTER	8	◇
248. ON THE MAP	2	◇
123 **249.** BY GUM!	4	◇
250. A CRACKING PUZZLE	10	◇

TOTAL FOR THIS ROUND ◇

+ Bonuses (5 points each) ◇

+ Running total from previous round ◇

TOTAL SO FAR ◈
(carry forward to next round)

Here are four disks. On each disk there are four magnets which are in the shape of letters. No matter how you move or rotate the circles, the lightly shaded parts of the magnets always point towards the Magnetic North.

Rearrange and rotate the disks as necessary so that a 4 × 4 word square is formed, giving a total of eight 4-letter words.

CASH AND GRAB

"I'm going to let you win some money but it won't be easy!" promises Visual Vern.

"Here are 24 bags of cash and you can take any bags you like subject to a condition – as soon as I can take a bag of money which is halfway between two empty spaces, you lose any money you have taken and the game is over.

"For example, if you took bags A and B, you would lose because I can take bag X which is halfway between A and B."

How many bags would you dare to take?

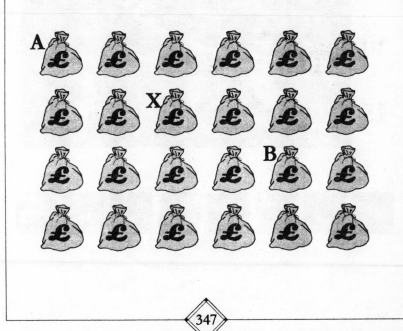

Using the aid of the picture, some simple
arithmetic, and a very well known letter code, can
you decide which 8-letter word is represented at the
bottom of the page?

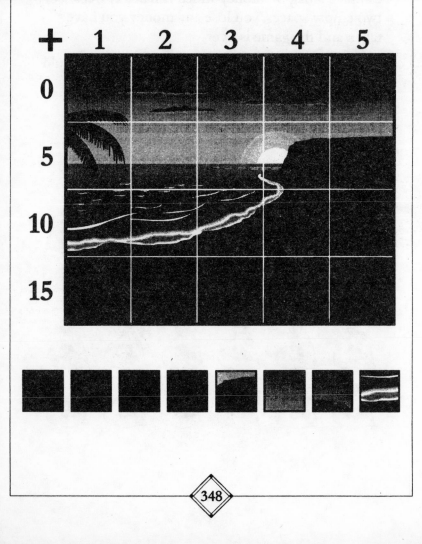

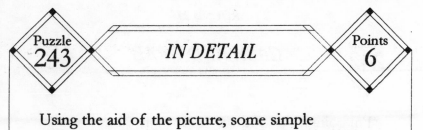

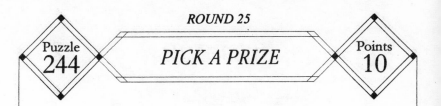

PICK A PRIZE

Here are eleven rings. However, only ring 5 is real – the rest are fakes. You must pick up a starting ring, then continue by removing every fifth ring counterclockwise around the circle. You only get to keep the last (eleventh) ring you pick up.

Without resorting to trial and error, how can you win the real ring using a maximum of two attempts?

Here are four pieces. When placed together, they form a well-known symbol.

Where two *differently* shaded pieces touch, each pair of touching squares either shares their shapes or numbers in common. For example, a star with a "2" on it must touch a star or a symbol with a "2" if it is adjacent to a differently shaded piece.

How should the pieces be arranged? No rotation of the pieces is necessary.

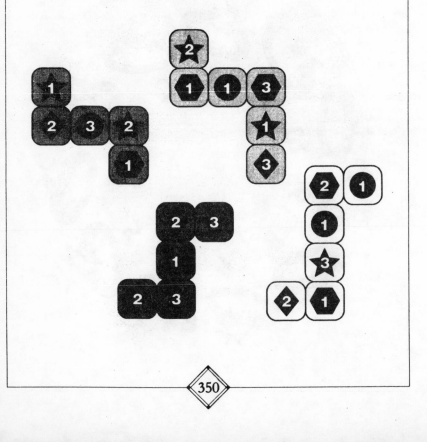

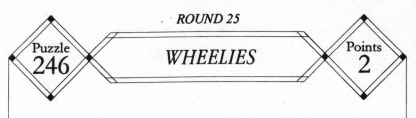

WHEELIES

A 13-letter word has been written on some wooden disks. However, the disks have been displaced slightly from their original positions.

Despite this, can you read what the word is?

"Tell me a number," demands Mandy Math. "It can be any integer number, which means negatives are allowed but fractions are not.

"Now, I bet I can name a number, which may have to be a fraction, so that our numbers multiplied together give the same result as your number minus twice my number."

You try a few numbers but she always manages to find a number satisfying the above criterion.

However, you manage to spot a way to defeat her. What is the only number that will allow you to beat Mandy?

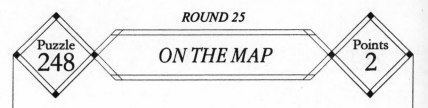

When the carnival owner returned from a holiday
he brought back a few mementoes.

Can you work out what at least six of the seven
box labels refer to?

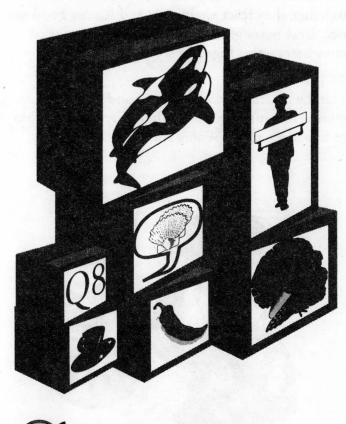

If you can name all seven,
collect 5 bonus points.

BY GUM!

Sudbury's Supergum has arrived at the carnival. This substance possesses some remarkable abilities which allows for much more chewing time than ordinary gum.

For example, if three used banana gums are put together, they react chemically and form a good-as-new strawberry gum. Likewise, putting two used strawberry gums together form a brand-new banana gum.

Tommy has 19 strawberry gums and 15 banana gums. How many gums will he enjoy before he has to buy some more of this amazing candy?

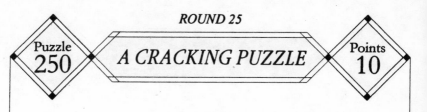

A CRACKING PUZZLE

At the fairground's Chinese food stall, Hong Kong Harry is entertaining his diners.

"I'll make a bet with you. Watch this," he says. He takes a chopstick and breaks it into three. He arranges the pieces into a triangle.

"If you can do that, it counts as a win. If you can't make a triangle, then I win. OK, who wants to bet that, if we break the chopstick randomly at any two points along its length, you can make a triangle with the three pieces formed?"

What odds should Harry offer to ensure that this is a fair bet – that is, the odds are fair to both Harry and the player?

241.

242. The most you can take is four bags. For the sake of an example, suppose you took the top-left bag and the three bags surrounding it. You can no longer take any other bag without leaving a middle bag for Vern to snatch. (The principle of this puzzle lies in odd and even numbers on either axis, hence 2 × 2 = 4 bags maximum.)

243. Adding the coordinates for each square means the squares are numbered sequentially from 1 to 5 along the top row, down to 16 to 20 along the bottom row. We use the old A=1, B=2 etc. code. The first picture is a detail from square 20 (15+5), so that decodes as T (because T is the 20th letter). Repeating this for every square leads to the word TROPICAL.

244. Do a trial run by removing ring 1 first and continue to see where you end up. By crossing off each ring as we pick it up, we remove 7, 2, 6, 10, 3, 4, 11, 8, 5 which leaves ring 9. (When counting in fives, remember not to count rings once they have been picked up.) Since starting at position 1 meant we ended up in position 9, then (by moving four places counterclockwise) it follows that starting at position 8 will leave us with the prize ring at position 5. So position 8 is the correct answer.

245. A cross is formed:

246. The word REVOLUTIONARY can be read. The middles of the letters have been rotated about 30 degrees clockwise. The bottom parts have been rotated a further 30 degrees.

247. Suppose our number is called a and Mandy's number is called b. Translating the question into algebra, we get:

$$ab = a - 2b$$
$$ab + 2b = a$$
$$b(a + 2) = a$$
$$b = \frac{a}{a + 2}$$

If we select a to be -2, the bottom line of the fraction becomes zero which means that the whole fraction does not exist. (Any fraction with zero as the denominator is not defined in mathematics.)

248. The labels refer to the countries from which each souvenir came. We have China (china teacup), Kuwait (Q–8), Chile (chilli), Seychelles (say 'shells'), Turkey, Wales (whales) and finally Korea (because the man with a parcel is a 'courier'... ouch!)

249. The best solution I could find was 57 whole gums:

Banana	Strawberry		
15	19	Eat 18 strawberry	(leftovers makes 9 banana)
24	1	Eat 24 banana	(leftovers makes 8 strawberry)
0	9	Eat 8 strawberry	(leftovers makes 4 banana)
4	1	Eat 3 banana	(leftovers makes 1 strawberry)
1	2	Eat 2 strawberry	(leftovers makes 1 banana)
2	0	Eat 2 banana	(leftovers can't make anything else)

Total : 29 banana, 28 strawberry.

250. The odds should be 4-to-1 for the game to be fair. Clearly, if any one of the pieces is over half a chopstick, the other two cannot possibly "close up" the triangle. The probability that any of the three parts is too large is equally likely. This probability is the same chance that all three parts are under half the original length. This gives four scenarios, only one of which is successful.

TEST YOUR STRENGTH

How are you doing? Calculate your score so far and
see how high you can try...

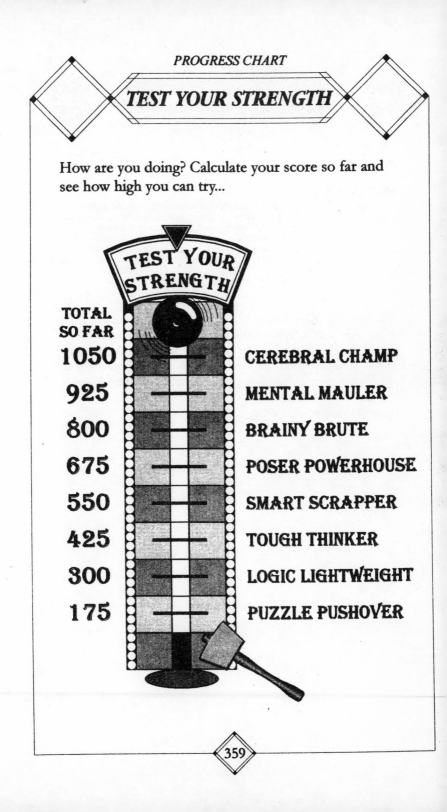

TOTAL
SO FAR

1050	CEREBRAL CHAMP
925	MENTAL MAULER
800	BRAINY BRUTE
675	POSER POWERHOUSE
550	SMART SCRAPPER
425	TOUGH THINKER
300	LOGIC LIGHTWEIGHT
175	PUZZLE PUSHOVER

ROUND 26

Use this page to keep track of your score. Carry your total
forward to the next round of puzzles.

Answers to Round 26 puzzles are on pages 372–4.

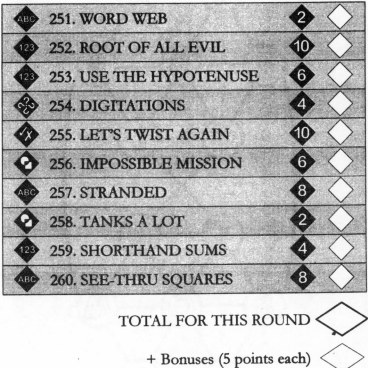

Category	Points	Your Score
ABC 251. WORD WEB	2	◇
123 252. ROOT OF ALL EVIL	10	◇
123 253. USE THE HYPOTENUSE	6	◇
254. DIGITATIONS	4	◇
255. LET'S TWIST AGAIN	10	◇
256. IMPOSSIBLE MISSION	6	◇
ABC 257. STRANDED	8	◇
258. TANKS A LOT	2	◇
123 259. SHORTHAND SUMS	4	◇
ABC 260. SEE-THRU SQUARES	8	◇

TOTAL FOR THIS ROUND ◇

+ Bonuses (5 points each) ◇

+ Running total from previous round ◇

TOTAL SO FAR ◇
(carry forward to next round)

Trace the longest word which can be found on this web.

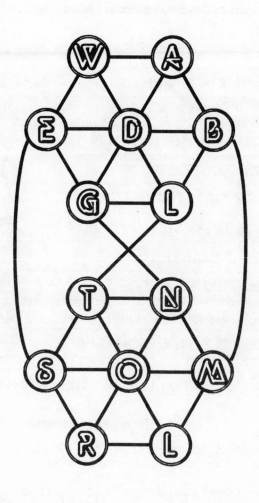

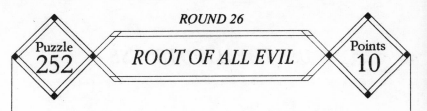

ROOT OF ALL EVIL

"I really hate the square root sign. I'm sure it causes more trouble than it's worth and moreover I don't think it's necessary," says Mandy Math, cryptically.

"For I never have to write that horrid sign. Instead, I use a fraction which continues for ever and ever.

"I'm thinking of a square root of a particular whole number. The usual way of writing it would need the square root sign, so instead I write it as:

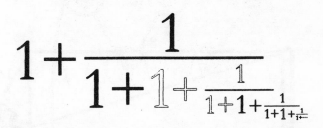

"Do you see how the pattern goes? You start with 'one plus one over one plus...' (in black) and then you keep going with another 'one plus one over one plus...' (in white) and so on.

"Now let's see if you've understood all that. To win the game, tell me what number I am thinking of."

BONUS Solve this additional puzzle for 5 bonus points:

How else could you have solved this puzzle?

A young visitor to the fairground is playing one of those infamous crane grab machines.

She turns to you and says "I never quite manage to hook one of the teddy bears. It would help if I knew how long the crane was."

The crane (not drawn to scale) is constructed from three strong, right-angled triangles. Given four of the sides, what is the length of the fifth?

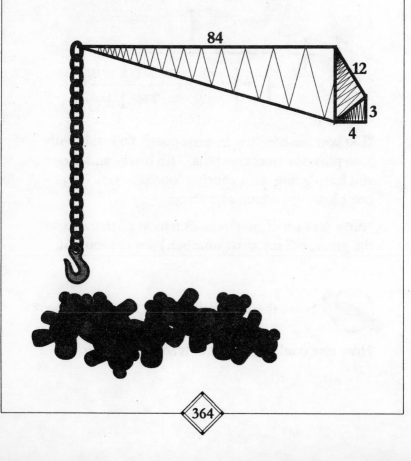

DIGITATIONS

Draw the next figure in this sequence:

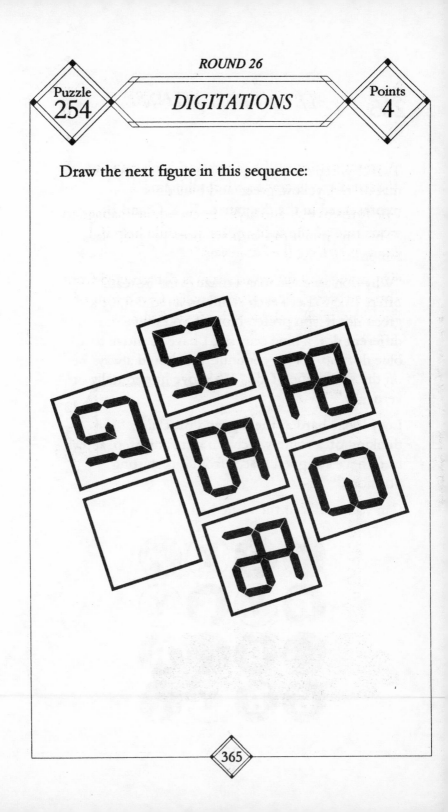

Two children are playing a party game which uses a mat of red, yellow, green and blue dots (represented in the diagram as R, Y, G and B).

"This isn't much fun without more people," says Simon.

"Why don't we use it as a maze game instead?" offers Lucy. "Let's each stand on a red dot, or a green dot if you prefer. Now, if you move onto a different dot, a blue one, say, I have to move to a blue dot too. As we continue, we should always be on the same type of dot. We move horizontally or vertically."

Lucy looks hard at the mat and proclaims "I'm thinking of a route which, on our sixth step, allows us to have swapped places from our starting positions."

Can you work out the route had Lucy seen?

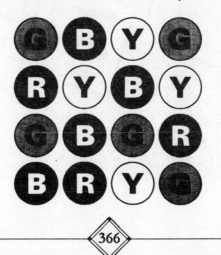

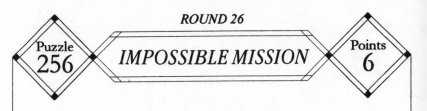

IMPOSSIBLE MISSION

"This is an impossible puzzle," says Visual Vern, "but I suppose they all seem that way at first!

"The spaceship has to travel through each space sector square, but it must avoid those containing the large planets so that there is no risk of being sucked into its gravitational field.

"They want to make as much progress as possible by visiting each square once only. It is impossible for them to visit every uninhabited square. What is the most they can achieve?"

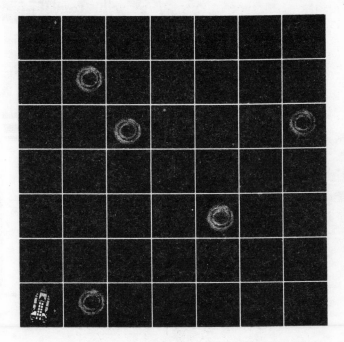

Here are six pieces of woven fabric. At the moment, you can see the backs of each strip.

Each piece has the end nearest the square nailed down. The rest of the fabric is free-moving.

How can you weave the strands so that a 3 × 3 word square is formed in the box?

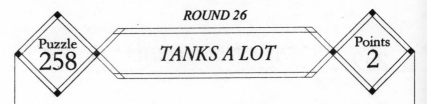

Sam the Performing Sealion has a large tank which is held together by long metal rods and canvas panels.

When completely full it can store 1000 gallons of water. This is what it looks like:

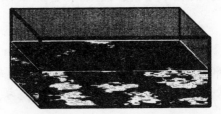

Or, rather, that's what it used to look like. One day, after he had performed his act, Sam came back to find this:

Someone had changed it so that, although it had the same length, width and perpendicular height, the walls sloped at a 30 degree angle.

What is the maximum amount of water the tank can hold now?

Mandy Math's son, Norman Numbers, is experimenting with something he's been shown at school.

"I'm using a new symbol to simplify my calculations," explains Norman. "For example, the number of ways you can arrange a pack of cards is:

$$52 \times 51 \times 50 \times 49 \times \cdots \times 4 \times 3 \times 2 \times 1$$

"That's a huge calculation, not to mention a huge number, so I just write the symbol shown here:

$$\underline{52} = 52 \times 51 \times 50 \times 49 \times \cdots \times 4 \times 3 \times 2 \times 1$$

"Likewise:

$$\underline{3} + \underline{5} = (3 \times 2 \times 1) + (5 \times 4 \times 3 \times 2 \times 1) = 126$$

"For my own reasons, $\underline{0}$ is defined to equal 1."

What does the sum below add up to?

 Solve this additional puzzle for 5 bonus points:

Once you've worked out the principle behind the puzzle above, can you find the only other number (apart from 1 and 2) which possesses the evident property?

Free hint: All its three digits are under 6.

SEE-THRU SQUARES

Wordsmith Will is having a hard time. "I made up this puzzle years ago but I can't remember the solution. Maybe you could help me.

"I remember that you are supposed to take the four grids and put them one above the other so that, when you look down through the grids, a 4 × 4 word square is formed. But as you can see, I haven't been able to get the answer yet."

What is the solution Will intended years ago?

Looking down through the grids in the direction shown by the arrow currently gives:

251. The longest word possible is the word LONGEST.

252. There are two ways of cracking this. The really easy way is to approximate. For instance, if we evaluate as far as the third iteration:

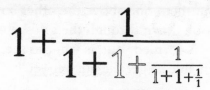

$$1 + \cfrac{1}{1 + 1 + \cfrac{1}{1 + 1 + \frac{1}{1}}}$$

the answer is 1.42857. This is already very close to the square root of 2, so Mandy was thinking of the number 2 (or –2).

The harder way is to use a formula. Because the process iterates over and over again, you should be able to see how the first line of the following calculation is the same thing as the never-ending fraction:

$$x = 1 + \tfrac{1}{1+x}$$
$$\tfrac{x(1+x)}{1+x} = \tfrac{1+x}{1+x} + \tfrac{1}{1+x}$$
$$x(1+x) = x + 2$$
$$x + x^2 = x + 2$$
$$x^2 = 2$$
$$\therefore x = \sqrt{2} \text{ (or } \sqrt{-2})$$

253. This puzzle requires you to use Pythagoras' Theorem repeatedly:

$$3^2 + 4^2 = 25 = 5^2$$
$$5^2 + 12^2 = 169 = 13^2$$
$$13^2 + 84^2 = 7225 = 85^2$$

Hence the fifth length of the crane is 85 units long.

ANSWERS

254. The symbol (below left) completes the sequence. If the diagram is rotated 70 degrees counterclockwise and we prise the symbols apart (below right), everything becomes clear:

255. The children start, and end up on, the red dots shown:

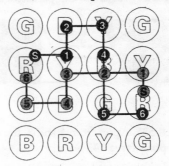

256. It is possible to cover all but two squares. For example:

257. Weave the strands as shown:

258. It still holds 1000 gallons. The diagram explains why: The same holds true for any rectangle and parallelogram.

Same area

259. The total is 40585. Apart from 1 and 2, the other number which holds this property is 145 because:

$$\langle 1 \rangle + \langle 4 \rangle + \langle 5 \rangle = (1) + (4 \times 3 \times 2 \times 1) + (5 \times 4 \times 3 \times 2 \times 1)$$
$$= 145$$

260. Put 3 on the top, then 4, then 2, then 1 on the bottom. This gives:

ROUND 27

Use this page to keep track of your score. Carry your total forward to the next round of puzzles.

Answers to Round 27 puzzles are on pages 386–8.

Category		Points	Your Score
	261. ANYTHING YOU CAN DO...	4	◇
	262. CROSSFIRE	10	◇
	263. PRIZES GALORE	6	◇
	264. RACE TRACK	6	◇
	265. VOLUME DOWN	4	◇
	266. WORD-CROSS	8	◇
	267. KNIGHT'S TOUR	2	◇
	268. SQUARE WORDS	8	◇
	269. KNIT WITS	2	◇
	270. MEASURE FOR MEASURE	10	◇

TOTAL FOR THIS ROUND ◇

+ Bonuses (5 points each) ◇

+ Running total from previous round ◇

TOTAL SO FAR ◆
(carry forward to next round)

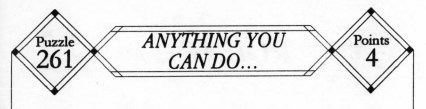
The cat is trying to catch the mouse. Every time the cat moves, the mouse always makes the opposite move. For example, if the cat moves two positions east, the mouse moves two positions west.

At how many places can the cat can catch the mouse?

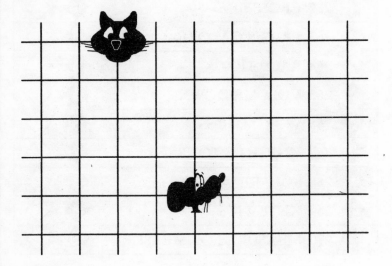

 Solve this additional puzzle for 5 bonus points:

Suppose instead that the mouse always moves in the direction 90 degrees clockwise to the direction the cat takes. If they start at the same places shown above, at which point can the cat catch the mouse now?

CROSSFIRE

Place two vowels somewhere inside the circle, and draw three more straight lines, so that two 4-letter and eight 3-letter words can be read.

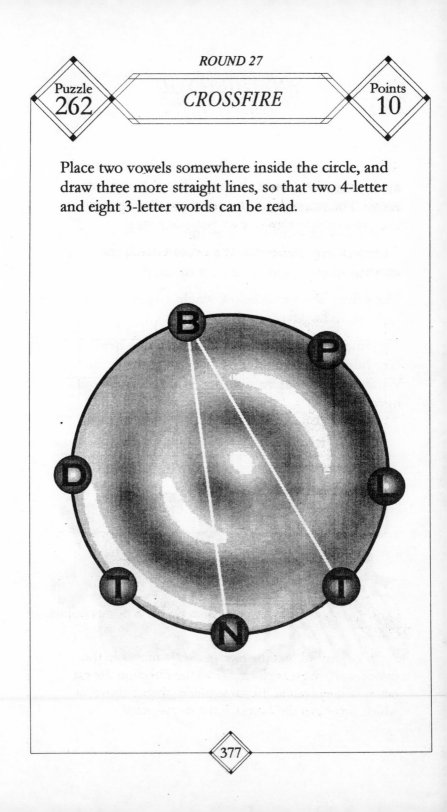

PRIZES GALORE

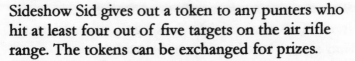

Sideshow Sid gives out a token to any punters who hit at least four out of five targets on the air rifle range. The tokens can be exchanged for prizes.

A bottle of champagne takes four times as many tokens as a teddy bear, and a teddy bear takes three times as many tokens as a stick of candy.

The prizes illustrated below would require a grand total of 782 tokens.

Mr Jameson's daughter would like a teddy bear to take home as a reminder of her day at the carnival. What is the minimum number of targets he would have to hit?

RACE TRACK

"This is a race track for toy cars," explains Visual Vern. "Two cars are put into the grid at high speed. They always travel in a straight line unless one of the bends changes their direction.

"Assuming the cars don't crash at a crossover point, of which there are many, the cars will emerge having turned through a total of 540 degrees; that's one-and-a-half turns. One car always turns left, the other car always turns right.

"Place the spare bends onto the ground so that the cars will emerge at the exit points."

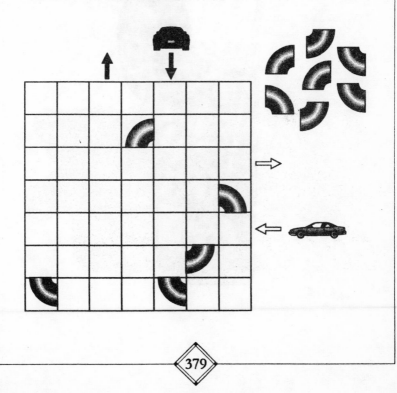

"Have a drink," offers Visual Vern. "But before you drink it, here's a puzzle for you to solve.

"Suppose I take out some liquid from the glass so that it is exactly half full. Without resorting to the use of any equipment, how can you reduce the amount so that, without going pedantic extremes, it is exactly one-quarter full?"

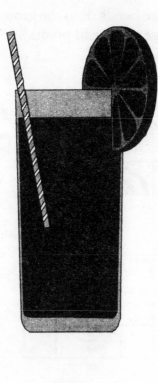

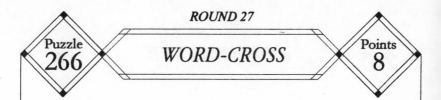

WORD-CROSS

Wordsmith Will introduces his latest puzzle. "You've heard of crosswords. Well this is a word-cross.

"Any two consecutive letter pairs around the cross form a four-letter word. For example, I've started you off with SKID, IDEA, and EACH.

"To win the game, continue in the same fashion so that the word-cross is complete. Use the letter pairs provided. Each pair is only used once."

Most chess players have heard of the Knight's Tour where the knight visits all 64 squares of the chessboard.

There are several different ways this can be done.

Is it possible to devise a route so that the knight starts in one corner and finishes up in the opposite corner?

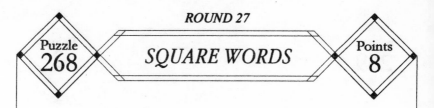

SQUARE WORDS

Each of these square rings can accommodate four letters along each side, so that a 12-letter word can be written clockwise in each ring, the first letter resting in the circle.

Where two rings overlap, the same letter is used in the word from either ring.

The 12-letter word in the bottom ring means "to disable". The middle ring means "cleverness". The darkest ring is a type of shop.

What are the three words?

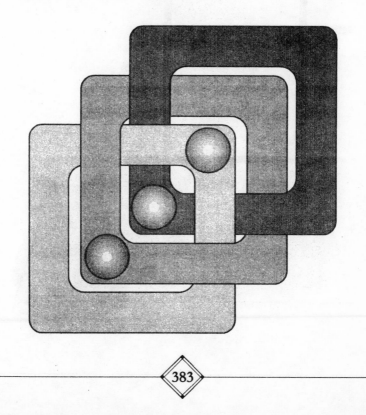

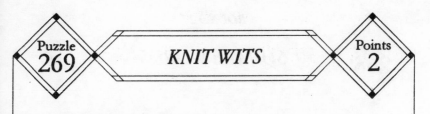

Mystic Molly wants to put her balls of wool onto this square of knitting needles so that her cat, Mischief, can't get at them.

She has fourteen balls of yarn and she would like to have the same number of balls on each side of the square so that she can tell at a glance if there has been any feline intervention.

How can she do it?

"I had a bit of a disaster earlier on this week," says a sad Baker Bill. "The carnival owner asked me to cook a magnificent cake to celebrate the carnival's golden anniversary. Here's some of the ingredients I was using:

Ingredients for
Golden Celebration Cake

1 ton of plain flour
2 bushels of castor sugar
1 peck of yeast
1 gallon of egg whites
20 fluid oz of egg yolks
15 pints of skimmed milk
2 stones of cream cheese
3 quarts of water
1oz gold leaf (for decoration)
P.T.O.

"I followed the cooking instructions to the letter and someone of my experience doesn't make mistakes on projects of this scale.

"The cake was a complete mess – the consistency was completely wrong. I don't suppose you can tell me where I went wrong, can you?"

N.B. You don't need to be a cook to find the answer.

261. The only place they can meet is the point halfway along the line joining them (see below left). Bonus puzzle: The point is shown (below right). It can be calculated as follows: Connect the cat and mouse by a (solid) line, then draw the (dotted) perpendicular bisector of this line. Move the mouse slightly, then move the cat via the same route rotated clockwise by 90 degrees. Then draw another pair of lines. The required point is where the two dotted lines cross.

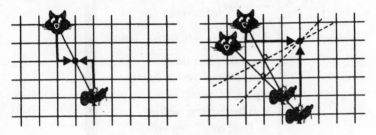

262. The words are BIN, NIB, PIT, TIP, PAN, NAP, LAID, DIAL, TAB and BAT:

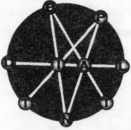

263. Let's express everything in terms of candy canes. One bottle of champagne is equivalent to 12 candy canes, so three bottles equals 36 canes. Also, two teddy bears equals 6 canes. So 4 canes + 3 bottles + 2 bears = 4 + 36 + 6 = 46 canes. Because this takes 782 tokens, this means it takes 782 / 46 = 17 tokens for one cane. Therefore a teddy bear costs 51 tokens, so Mr Jameson would need to hit 51 × 4 = 204 targets.

264.

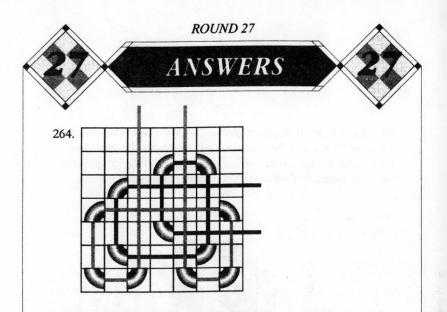

265. Hold the glass so that your thumbnail marks where the water level is. Tilt the glass so that the liquid touches the bottom edge. Then suck the drink through the straw until the water level is on a line between the bottom edge and the thumb position.

266.

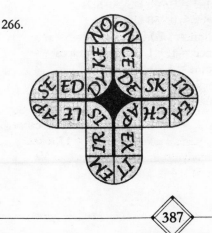

267. No, it's clearly not possible because the knight will alternate between black and white squares along his route. If there are 64 squares on the board, an even number, he must therefore finish on a black square if he started on a white one and vice versa.

268. The words are INCAPACITATE, INTELLIGENCE and DELICATESSEN:

269. Place three balls of yarn on each needle, and an extra one on two opposite corners. This makes four balls on every needle.

270. The recipe was from an American cook book but Bill was using the British measurements (or vice versa). In the case of the gold leaf, Bill forgot that gold was measured in troy ounces, not avoirdupois ounces.

1 UK ton = 1.12 US tons
1 UK bushel = 0.968 US bushels
1 UK peck = 0.968 US pecks
1 UK gallon = 1.20 US gallons
1 UK fluid ounce = 1.041 US fluid ounces
1 UK pint = 1.20 US pints
1 UK hundredweight = 1.12 US hundredweight
1 UK quart = 1.20 US quarts

ROUND 28

Use this page to keep track of your score. Carry your total forward to the next round of puzzles.

Answers to Round 28 puzzles are on pages 400–2.

Category	Points	Your Score
ABC 271. LINKING RINGS	8	◇
272. SQUARE DEAL	10	◇
273. FILL-UP	6	◇
123 274. SHOOT FOR THE HOOP	8	◇
275. PICTURE PUZZLE	4	◇
276. NEARLY	4	◇
277. MATCH THIS	2	◇
278. LONG DIVISION	6	◇
123 279. BOUNCE	2	◇
ABC 280. DOUBLING DICE	10	◇

TOTAL FOR THIS ROUND ◇

+ Bonuses (5 points each) ◇

+ Running total from previous round ◇

TOTAL SO FAR ◆
(carry forward to next round)

"See if you can work this little conundrum out," teases Wordsmith Will.

"Each of the circles on these rings contains a letter. The circles 12345 in the black ring on the far left spell out a word meaning 'faculty of speech'. The letters in the circles 67890 on the dark ring on the far right make a five letter word meaning 'little'.

"The lower-left ring carries a 6-letter word meaning 'opened', whereas the lower-right ring has an adverb connected with the meaning 'dry'. Both these words can be read in counterclockwise fashion.

"Tell me, what word can be read counterclockwise on the white ring?"

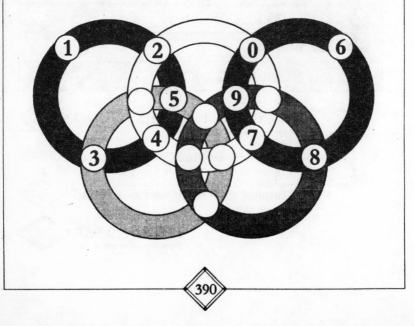

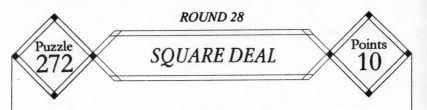

"This set of matchsticks has 30 squares," explains Visual Vern. "There are 16 small ones, nine 2 × 2 squares, four 3 × 3 ones, and a large 4 × 4 square.

"What is the least number of matches you need to remove from this set-up so that none of these squares, of any size, can be seen?"

Visual Vern is challenging Lateral Larry to a puzzle shoot-out. "See if you can solve this one, Larry," he says.

"I have a 7 × 7 board (with a hole in the middle) which I want to cover with the black shapes. There are eleven L-shaped pieces, and one piece that looks a bit like an S. This is enough to cover the 48 squares."

"I'm not even going to attempt it," snorts Larry. "Instead, give me a puzzle that's possible to complete!"

How did Larry deduce that Vern's puzzle was impossible?

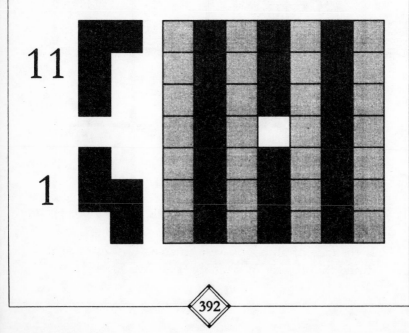

11

1

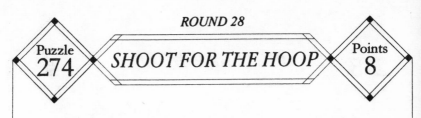

Puzzle
274

SHOOT FOR THE HOOP

Points
8

In this game you have to throw a 2ft-wide beach ball through one of the two smaller hoops without it touching the sides. The radii of the hoops are 4, 8 and 12 feet.

Assuming that the ball is thrown so that its midpoint passes through the largest hoop at random, what are your chances of winning?

Solve this additional puzzle for 5 bonus points:

If the radii of all hoops were enlarged by 6.25%, what would the chances of winning be increased to?

Colin the Clown shows you this puzzling picture of his brother.

Use the grid to help work out his name.

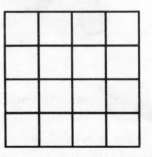

What 7-letter word is almost represented here?

"I've got another one of those traditional matchstick puzzles for you," says Visual Vern. "As you can see, I have a set of matchsticks laid out to make a spiral. By moving only four matches, how can you form three squares?"

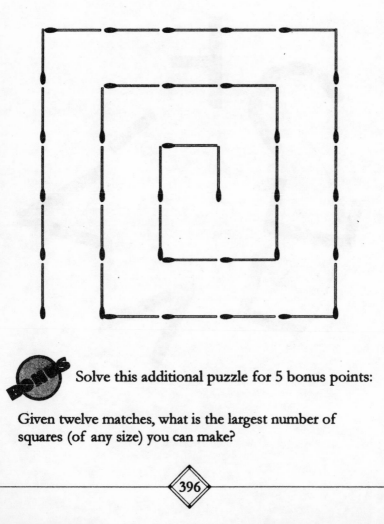

Solve this additional puzzle for 5 bonus points:

Given twelve matches, what is the largest number of squares (of any size) you can make?

LONG DIVISION

How can these letters be divided up using three
circles (which may overlap) so that each letter is
separated from all the other letters?

In other words, you must not be able to move from
one letter to any other without crossing a line.

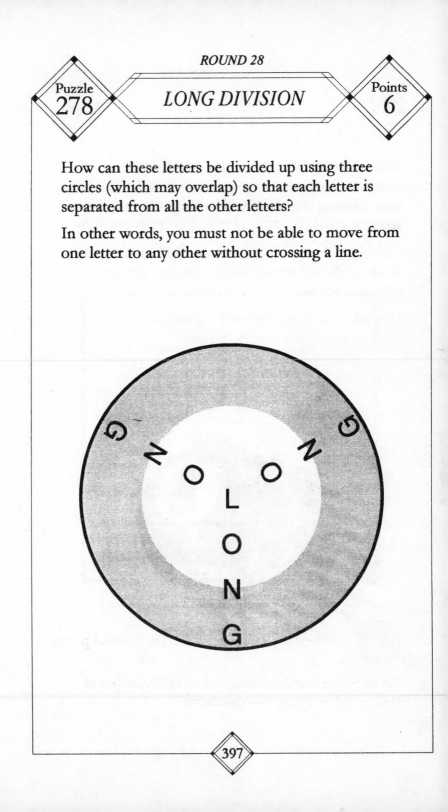

BOUNCE

While playing in the fairground's pool hall, Sideshow Sid gets distracted and makes a terrible shot, causing the black ball to jump 4½ feet in the air.

On each subsequent bounce, the ball rises to one tenth of the maximum height reached by the previous bounce.

In total, how many feet will the ball have covered when it eventually comes to rest?

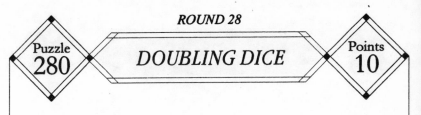

Puzzle
280

DOUBLING DICE

Points
10

Wordsmith Will is playing with a pair of dice. "I've just thrown two sixes. See if you can fill in the dice using these clues," he says.

To win the game, complete the puzzle. You have to work out which clue in each pair fits in which of the crosswords.

ACROSS
1. Outer boundary (7); 0°C (3,4)
5. Perpetually young; Like an ass
9. Least; Generally applicable
10. Gas; Copy
11. Genius; Regard

DOWN
1. Skip briskly; Think of
2. Post meridian; Decayed
3. Bring to life; Use
4. Go lower; Pure substance
6. Jewel; Knight
7. Allow; Pinch
8. Holy woman; To pose

271. The words are VOICE, SMALL, PRISED and ARIDLY.
The word around the white ring is OLYMPICS:

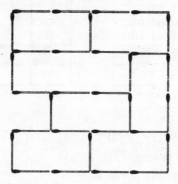

272. Nine matches is the minimum:

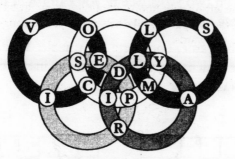

273. The L-shape pieces, no matter where they are placed on the board, will always cover one square of one shade and three squares of another, e.g. 1 light and 3 dark squares. As there are an odd number of L-shapes, then the number of light and dark squares covered in total will be odd for either shade. The single S-shaped piece does nothing to change this. As we start off with an even number of both shades, and yet we have covered an odd number for both shades, then the puzzle is impossible.

274. We know that the middle of the ball will pass somewhere within the hoop with 12-yard radius. To win, the ball has to go through the left or right hoop without touching the sides. Therefore, the midpoint of the ball has to pass through a circle of radius 3 or 7 yards.

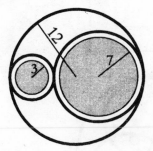

So, using the formula for the area of a circle, the chance that the centre of the ball will fall in one of the desired places is:

$$\frac{\pi 3^2 + \pi 7^2}{\pi 12^2} = \frac{9 + 49}{144} = \frac{29}{72} \approx 0.4$$

Therefore, the chance is 40%. The bonus answer is 50%.

275. When the jigsaw is reassembled, the letters on the tiles form the message MY NAME'S GARIBALDI.

276. One line from each letter of FLANKED was missing:

277.

(Other similar results are also possible.)

278.

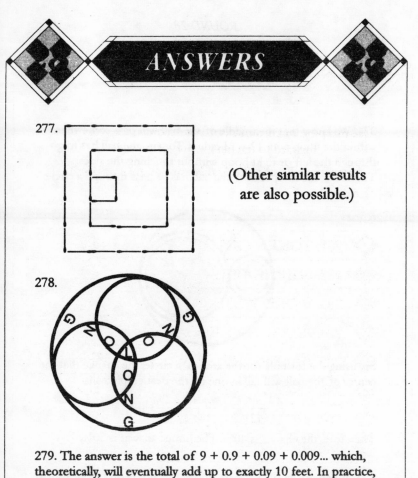

279. The answer is the total of 9 + 0.9 + 0.09 + 0.009... which, theoretically, will eventually add up to exactly 10 feet. In practice, it will be just short of 10 feet.

280

S	U	R	F	A	C	E
C		U		N		L
A	S	I	N	I	N	E
M	I	N	I	M	U	M
P	R	O	P	A	N	E
E		U		T		N
R	E	S	P	E	C	T

I	C	E	C	O	L	D
M		V		P		E
A	G	E	L	E	S	S
G	E	N	E	R	I	C
I	M	I	T	A	T	E
N		N		T		N
E	G	G	H	E	A	D

ROUND 29

Use this page to keep track of your score. Carry your total forward to the next round of puzzles.

Answers to Round 29 puzzles are on pages 414–16.

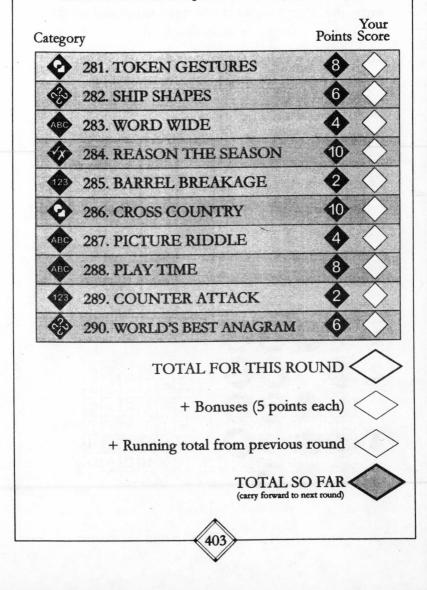

Category	Points	Your Score
281. TOKEN GESTURES	8	◇
282. SHIP SHAPES	6	◇
283. WORD WIDE	4	◇
284. REASON THE SEASON	10	◇
285. BARREL BREAKAGE	2	◇
286. CROSS COUNTRY	10	◇
287. PICTURE RIDDLE	4	◇
288. PLAY TIME	8	◇
289. COUNTER ATTACK	2	◇
290. WORLD'S BEST ANAGRAM	6	◇

TOTAL FOR THIS ROUND ◇

+ Bonuses (5 points each) ◇

+ Running total from previous round ◇

TOTAL SO FAR ◆
(carry forward to next round)

TOKEN GESTURES

"Here are some numbered tokens, five of each shade," explains Visual Vern. "They have to be placed in the 5 by 5 box in such a way that the same shade or number is not used more than once in any row, column or main diagonal.

"I've placed a few chips to start you off. To win the game, complete the grid using the remaining tokens."

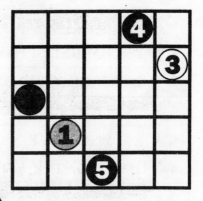

SHIP SHAPES

Using the code letters for the smaller ships as a
guide, what can you say about the name of the
large ship?

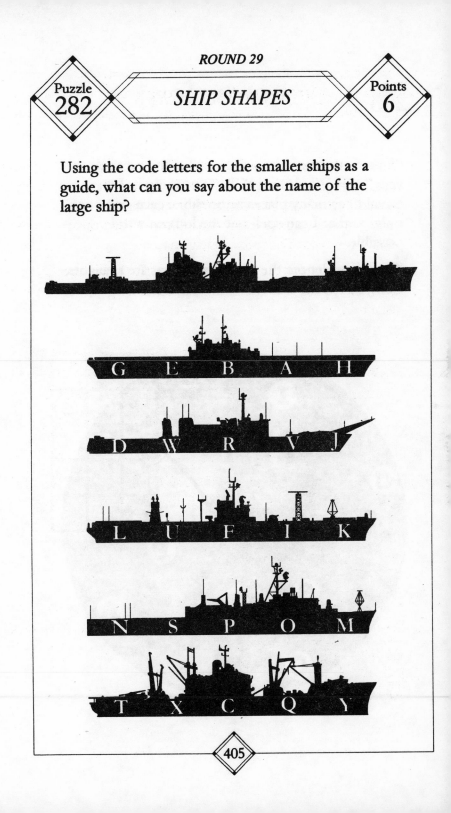

"Here is the map I'm using to plan my vacation this year," says Wordsmith Will. "The thing is, I want to travel to as many places as possible, each one once only, so that I can spell out the longest word possible.

"The lines denote the flight paths that are available. Can you tell me what route I should take?"

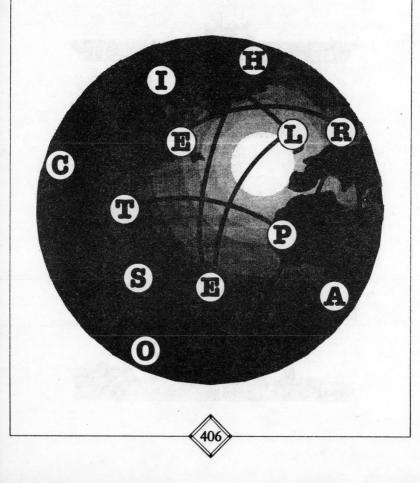

REASON THE SEASON

"This puzzle tests your powers of observation. It's so tough it'll knock you into the middle of next week," warns Lateral Larry.

"Here is a series of six words. They don't seem to have anything in common. Yet, there is one word, and only one word, that will continue the hidden logic.

"I'll even tell you that the word I'm looking for is the name of a season in the Christian calendar. Now does that help you?"

What word finishes the sequence?

COSMONAUT
STATUETTE
SWEDE
ENTHUSE
BOYFRIEND
VERSATILE
?

The carnival owner isn't very happy. It is coming up to winter time and he is down to his last barrel of heating oil.

Worse still, the full barrel has developed a leak, and the oil has spilled into the gap in between the barrels. A top-down view of the situation is shown below.

Each barrel is 1 yard in diameter. What is the area of the shaded region, now covered in oil?

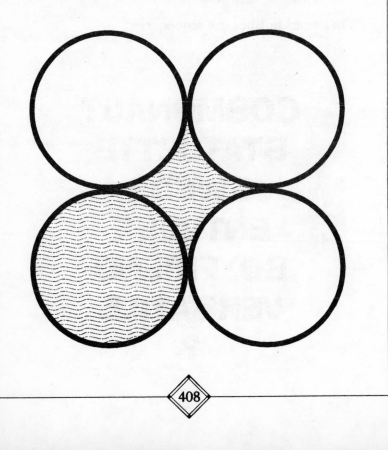

CROSS COUNTRY

"I have placed seven coins in this circle. However, only five of them are real. You have to eliminate the false pair," explains Mystic Molly.

"The way you do this is to draw a line between the centre of one circle to the centre of another. But I'm not going to tell you how to match them up — you've got to work the out the logic for yourself."

Which two coins are false?

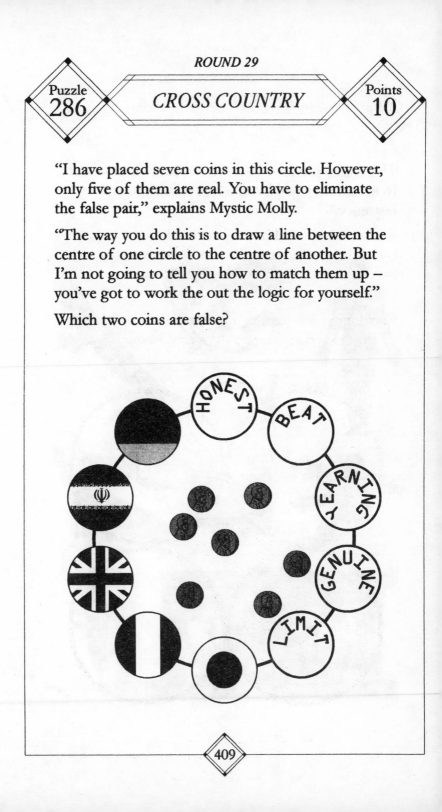

These nine pictures all represent four-letter words.
How can they be placed into a special, logical
sequence?

PLAY TIME

First examine the story below.

Then, if you were told that the narrator was called 1745, what would you say his name was?

I was walking down the street when I saw 4 billboard 13647 of me which was advertising 4 play.

"34!" I thought, "that's the 2456 play my friend 245 is in." 236 is not 4 brilliant actor, 4 real 345 if the truth be told, but I went to see it anyway.

The whole production was 4 complete 2345, which was 4 real 23456 because I knew 236 347 been rehearsing hard all week. 236 felt 517, 217 and 1234567 but 236 calmed down once we talked about it later, over 4 cup of 5647.

How can these counters be rearranged so that:

(a) no two counters with consecutive numbers are directly connected, and (b) the totals of the two diagonals indicated are equal?

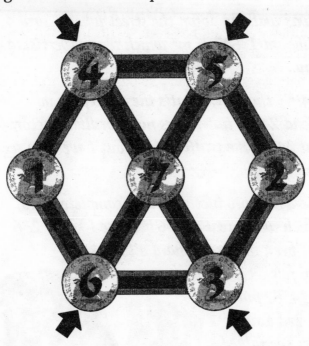

 Solve this additional puzzle for 5 bonus points:

This puzzle has several solutions. Give solutions where the diagonals total to the (i) highest, and (ii) lowest number possible.

THE WORLD'S
BEST ANAGRAM

"Many people through the ages of time have tried to construct truly brilliant anagrams," begins Wordsmith Will.

"One of the best anagrams I've come across recently are the words CINEMATOGRAPHER, as in a film maker, and MEGACHIROPTERAN, which is an adjective for a certain kind of butterfly.

"That's a very impressive anagram, but I think the one illustrated here is the world's best.

"Can you see how the given side of the equation can be rearranged in anagram fashion to provide a suitable sum on the other side?"

ONE + TWELVE = ?

281. Notice how the numbers cycle two spaces right each row, whereas the shades cycle two spaces left:

282. Comparing each part of the ship with the parts from the smaller ships, we find that the ship's name is DISCOVERY:

283. The longest word is HELICOPTER:

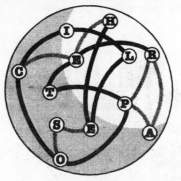

284. WHITSUNTIDE, because all the words have an abbreviation for a day of the week in the middle of them, i.e. cosMONaut, staTUEtte, sWEDe, enTHUse, and so on.

285. By rearranging the shape, we can see that the shaded area is one square yard:

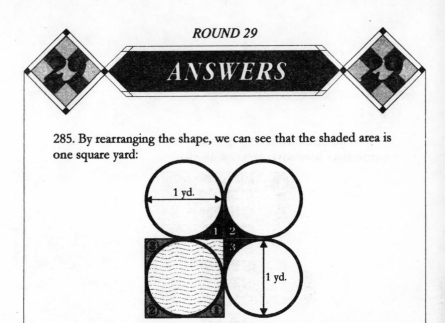

286. Each clue refers to the name of a currency, hence the reference to coins in the puzzle. For example, BEAT means POUND which is the currency of the UK, so we draw a line between these two circles. Likewise for the words HONEST = FRANK (Franc, France), GENUINE = REAL (Rial, Iran), YEARNING = YEN (Yen, Japan), and LIMIT = MARK (Mark, Germany). The lines cross over all coins but two. These are the false coins (arrowed).

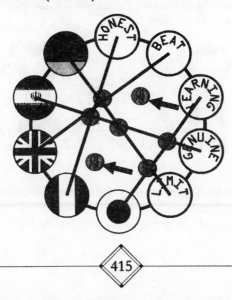

287. The words can be arranged into a word ladder, where one letter changes between each word, like so:

BROW
CROW
CHOW
CHOP
SHOP
SHIP
SLIP
SKIP
SKIN

288. Throughout the story, 1234567 = ASHAMED. So, for example, by substituting 1=A, 3=H, 6=E, 4=A and 7=D, then "...billboard 13647 of me" should be read as "...billboard AHEAD of me". Hence the narrator's name is ADAM.

289. The highest totals the diagonals can have is thirteen (see left diagram). The lowest is eleven (see right diagram). By choosing the numbers 3, 4 and 5 across the middle it is also possible to have twelve across the diagonals.

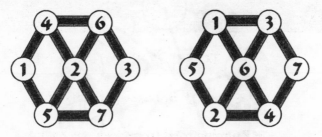

290. ONE + TWELVE = TWO + ELEVEN, which is a correct calculation.

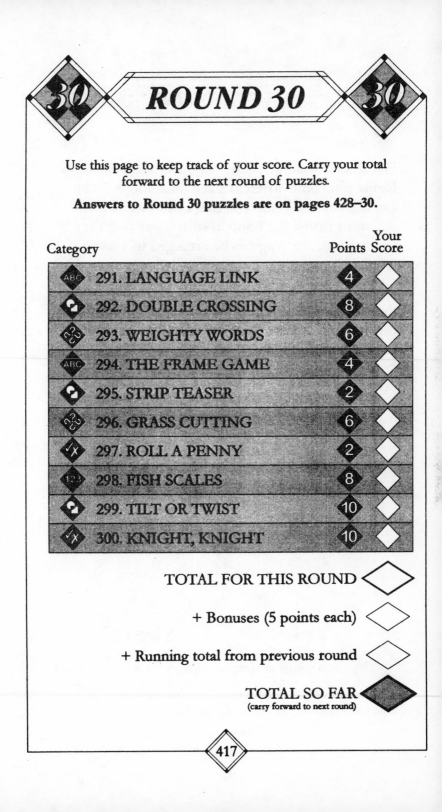

ROUND 30

Use this page to keep track of your score. Carry your total forward to the next round of puzzles.

Answers to Round 30 puzzles are on pages 428–30.

Category	Points	Your Score
291. LANGUAGE LINK	4	◇
292. DOUBLE CROSSING	8	◇
293. WEIGHTY WORDS	6	◇
294. THE FRAME GAME	4	◇
295. STRIP TEASER	2	◇
296. GRASS CUTTING	6	◇
297. ROLL A PENNY	2	◇
298. FISH SCALES	8	◇
299. TILT OR TWIST	10	◇
300. KNIGHT, KNIGHT	10	◇

TOTAL FOR THIS ROUND ◇

+ Bonuses (5 points each) ◇

+ Running total from previous round ◇

TOTAL SO FAR ◆
(carry forward to next round)

"Here, take hold of these," says Sideshow Sid as he hands you some different sized hula hoops. "You can use any size hoop you like, but to win a prize you must throw the hoop in such a way that the letters inside the ring can be arranged to make a word."

Given that the hoops are allowed to overlap (and thus use the same letters for different words), how can you win at least three prizes? All of the words have a common link.

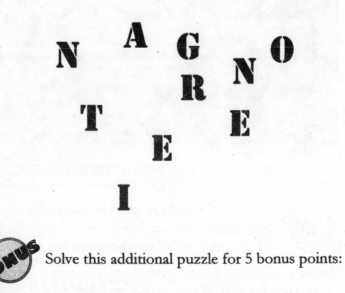

 Solve this additional puzzle for 5 bonus points:

Use two more hoops to win a total of five prizes.

DOUBLE CROSSING

Draw 12 straight lines through the crosses so that an X-shape is formed, with 20 crosses on the outside and 9 on the inside.

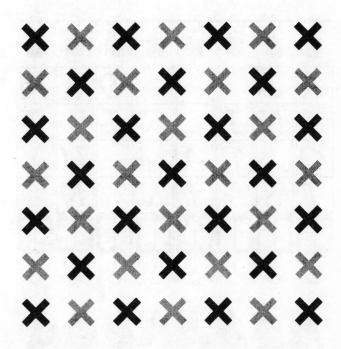

 Solve this additional puzzle for 5 bonus points:

Form a new cross (again using 12 lines) so that another X-shape is formed which has more crosses on the inside than there are on the outside.

Use the weights to lower each column of letters.

By using the right arrangement of weights, an 8-letter word can be read in the (fixed) black frames.

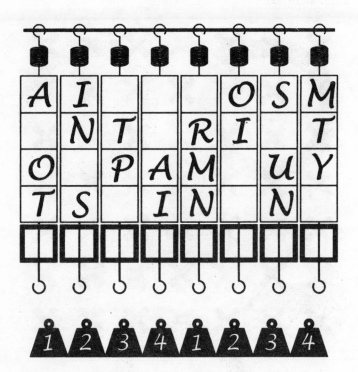

 Solve this additional puzzle for 5 bonus points:

Rearrange the weights again to find a related 8-letter word.

"I'm just trying to frame these three pictures with the black outers," explains Visual Vern.

"Can you tell me what logic I should use to frame each diagram?"

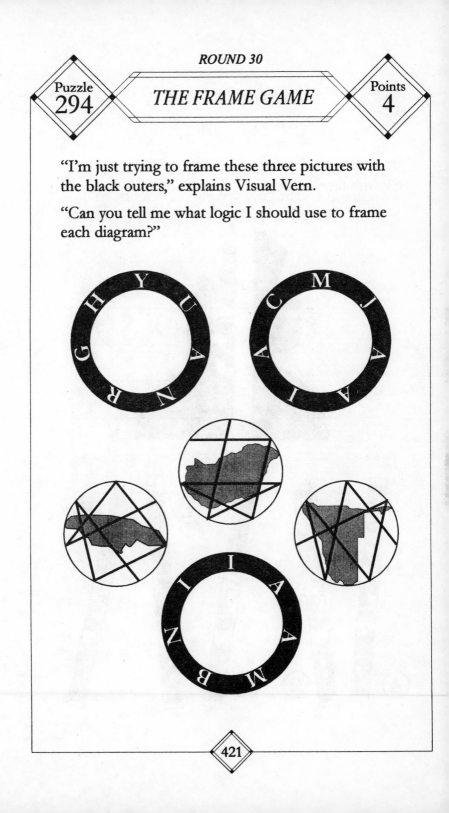

Which strip will help you complete Christopher Clown's face?

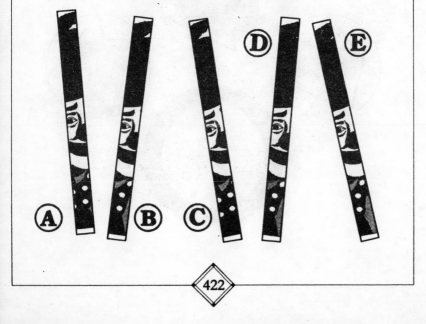

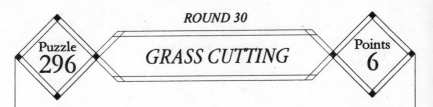

GRASS CUTTING

Harry, the fairground's green keeper, has a trusty old mower which he uses to keep the grass in trim.

Harry is getting on in years, and so is his mower. The machine travels well in a straight line, but when Harry wants to turn a corner he can only turn 90 degrees to the left.

Suppose Harry enters the garden below as shown and exits where the arrow indicates. What is the smallest number of left turns Harry will need so that every patch has been mown at least once?

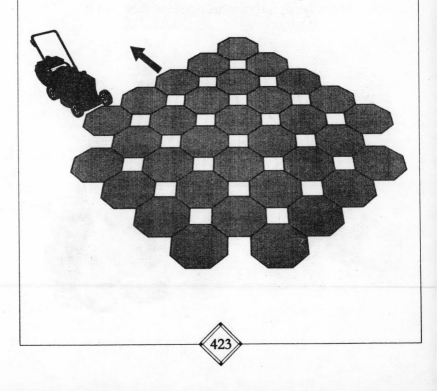

ROLL A PENNY

Mandy Math has just finished constructing her roll-a-penny stall. Actually, in this case, you roll silver coins.

As you can see from the diagram on the right, each square on the board is just large enough to hold four coins.

If you played this game, what reward for each winning coin would Mandy have to offer you before you'd consider this game to be fair? A coin wins if it lands within a square, without touching or crossing any lines.

Assume that the board is large enough so that your coin always lands successfully somewhere on it.

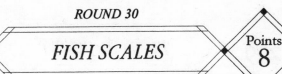

FISH SCALES

"There are three kinds of fish in them thar seas," says Fisherman Fred, pointing towards the coast.

"I know that three skillets weigh the same as four kipples and two darlets. I also know that six kipples and a darlet weigh the same as three skillets as well.

"If I were to multiply the weights, in pounds, of one for each kind of fish, I'd get 144 pounds.

"Can you tell me how heavy are the fish in these waters?"

Here is a tube containing four balls, two white and two black. The main tube can hold seven balls, although there is a small extra chamber which can hold one more ball.

There are two moves available to you:

i) Tilting the tube so that the balls roll to the opposite side.

ii) Twisting the tube through 180 degrees about the horizontal axis so that the extra chamber goes from the top to the underneath (or vice versa).

How many moves in total will it take so that the balls are in a row again but the black ones are to the right of the white ones, as we look at the tube?

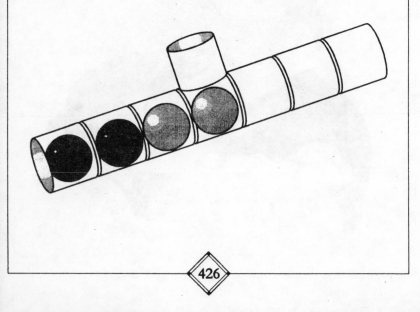

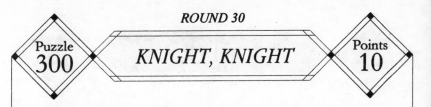

KNIGHT, KNIGHT

"This is the hardest puzzle I've ever devised," says Mystic Molly, "and it takes place on what remains of my smashed chess board."

"All you need to do is move the white knights onto the spaces with 'W' and the black knights onto the 'B' squares. Then find the least number of standard knight moves you'd need.

"You can jump over a smashed square, imagining it was still there, but of course you can't land a knight there."

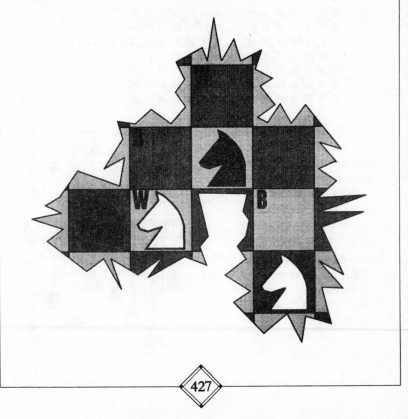

291. There were, in fact, a total of six prizes to be won. TAN, ORANGE and GREEN are fairly easy to spot. However, there is also TANGERINE, GARNET and its anagram ARGENT (the heraldic term for silver).

292.

293. The weights pull each column of letters down by the number of squares shown on the weight. By arranging the weights in a certain way, the word TITANIUM can be formed, as shown in the diagram.

Another metal, ANTIMONY, will show up in the black frames by rearranging the weights to read 4, 3, 3, 1, 2, 4, 1, 2 from left to right.

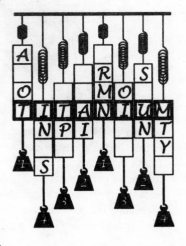

ANSWERS

294. By matching up the frames as follows, the black lines form a sequence, spelling out the names of HUNGARY, JAMAICA and NAMIBIA. (The shaded shapes are the coastlines of these countries.)

295. Strip B completes the picture.

296. Ten turns are necessary:

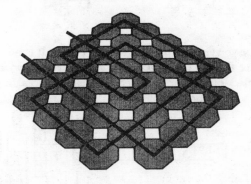

297. The diagram supplied in the question is all you need. The midpoint of the coins must lie in the shaded square which has side of 1 inch. If the midpoint of the coin lies in the unshaded part (which has a total area of 3 square inches) then the coin has to cross a line. So Mandy has to offer you odds of 3-to-1, i.e. 3 coins back for every winning coin.

298. It is fairly simple to deduce that $D = 2K$, and that $3S = 6K + D = 6K + 2K = 8K$ so $S = 8K/3$. So:

$$144 = S \times K \times D = \tfrac{8}{3} K \times K \times 2K = \tfrac{16}{3} K^3$$
$$\Leftrightarrow K^3 = \tfrac{144 \times 3}{16} = 27 \text{ so } K = 3 \text{ pounds}$$

It follows that D=6 and S=8.

299. Seven moves are required:

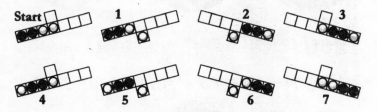

300. I hope you spotted the hint for this puzzle. It is no coincidence that the previous puzzle also concerns two white and two black pieces, and an object with eight spaces. In fact, we can make a correlation as follows:

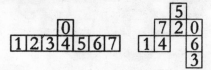

In both puzzles, the start and end positions are at the same numbers; and there is a "spare space" at 0.

The number of moves in the knight puzzle is equivalent to the number of squares the balls move in the tube puzzle. Hence the answer to the knight puzzle is 40 moves. This is the sum of 1 (move 1) + 12 (3 × 4; three balls move four squares in move 2) + 1 (move 3) + 12 (four balls × three squares in move 4) + 1 (move 5) + 12 (move 6) + 1 (move 7).

TEST YOUR STRENGTH

How are you doing? Calculate your score so far and
see how high you can try...

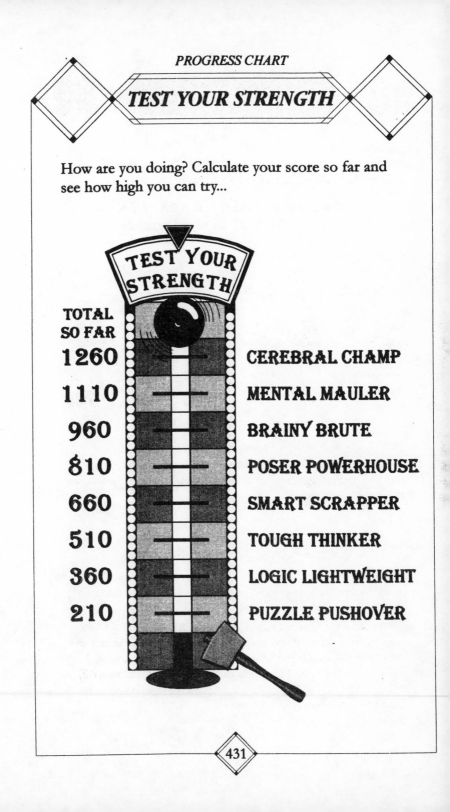

TEST YOUR STRENGTH

TOTAL SO FAR

1260	CEREBRAL CHAMP
1110	MENTAL MAULER
960	BRAINY BRUTE
810	POSER POWERHOUSE
660	SMART SCRAPPER
510	TOUGH THINKER
360	LOGIC LIGHTWEIGHT
210	PUZZLE PUSHOVER

ROUND 31

Use this page to keep track of your score. Carry your total forward to the next round of puzzles.

Answers to Round 31 puzzles are on pages 444–6.

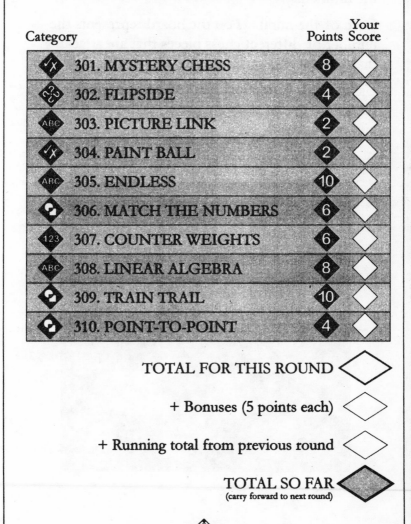

Category	Points	Your Score
301. MYSTERY CHESS	8	◇
302. FLIPSIDE	4	◇
303. PICTURE LINK	2	◇
304. PAINT BALL	2	◇
305. ENDLESS	10	◇
306. MATCH THE NUMBERS	6	◇
307. COUNTER WEIGHTS	6	◇
308. LINEAR ALGEBRA	8	◇
309. TRAIN TRAIL	10	◇
310. POINT-TO-POINT	4	◇

TOTAL FOR THIS ROUND ◇

+ Bonuses (5 points each) ◇

+ Running total from previous round ◇

TOTAL SO FAR ◆
(carry forward to next round)

MYSTERY CHESS

On the starred squares of this chessboard there are some chess pieces, although you can't see them at the moment.

Each of the numbers on the board represents the number of different chess pieces that are attacking that square.

Using this information, can you deduce which pieces are on the starred squares? None of the pieces are pawns.

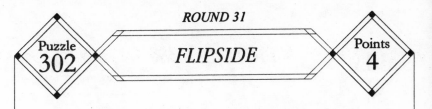

"Here's something for you to work out," says
Lateral Larry. "When I look at the number 4 in the
mirror, it looks like 6 and vice versa. When I look
at the number 9, it looks like 11. However, when I
look at the number 19, it doesn't look like 21."

What number does 19 look like when reversed?

4 ⬌ 6

9 ⬌ 11

19 ⬌ ?

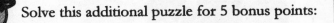

Solve this additional puzzle for 5 bonus points:

"Too easy?", asks Larry. "If so, consider the case of my
friend Roberta the Robot. If she looks at the number
10 in the mirror, it looks like 5. When she looks at the
number 6 reflected, it looks like 3. However, when she
looks at the number 8, it doesn't look like 4." What
number does 8 look like when reversed in this case?

What word links the following pictures?

PAINT BALL

Sideshow Sid has a new shooting game at his stall. It consists of a ball which floats in a column of air. As it does so, it spins around in random directions.

Sid hands the contestant a paintball gun with three red paint pellets. The player fires the pellets one at a time at the ball. If the three red pellets land in the same half of the ball, the contestant wins $16. On average, Side finds that contestants hit the target 50% of the time. The pellets are not heavy enough to dislodge the ball from the column of air.

What sum of money would you be prepared to pay to play the game so that it is statistically fair?

Puzzle 305

ENDLESS

Points 10

"Take a look at the following cryptic messages," offers Wordsmith Will. "If you can work out what the password is, you win the game."

Dress design = Chat

Round hall = Plump

War-horse = Cost

Brute = Skin discoloration

Muslim queen = Her husband

Medieval garment = Twice

Brave woman = Drug

Ashes = Stay

MATCH THE NUMBERS

What number should be matched with the final diagram?

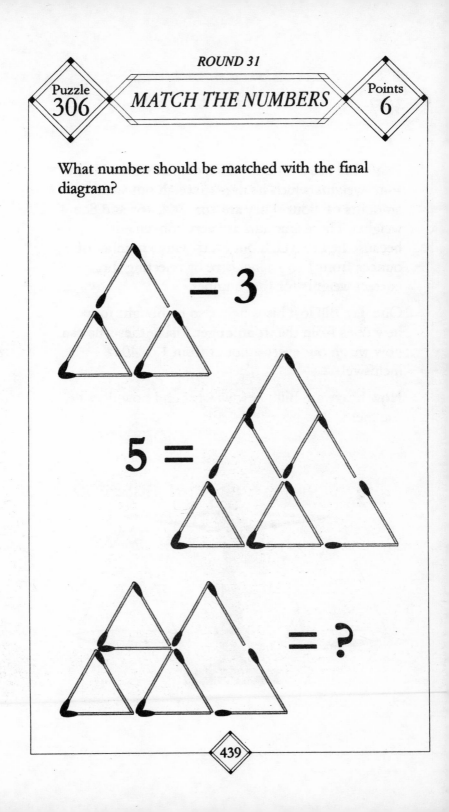

COUNTER WEIGHTS

Baker Bill has a traditional set of pan scales. He has four weights which he uses to weigh out various amounts of flour. They are 1oz, 2oz, 4oz and 8oz weights. These amounts are very convenient because he can weigh out every whole number of ounces from 1 to 15 inclusive by selecting the correct weights for that number.

One day, Bill lost his weights, so he bought four new ones from the ironmonger. Using these, he can now weigh out every amount from 1 to 40oz inclusive!

How heavy are Bill's new weights and how does he use them?

Puzzle
308

LINEAR ALGEBRA

Points
8

Examine the clues below, then work out which code number should be assigned to the 3-letter word.

Mend = ???

Two plus three = 3124

African country = 34333

Opposite to acid = 323321

Southeast Asian port = 433123

Live-in friend = 32324324

New York district = 433332233

Very strongly = 2434443223

Every day, the carnival owner travels from his house to the carnival via the city underground system.

Being rather an eccentric man, he ALWAYS travels EXACTLY four stops and then ALWAYS changes to a different line.

What is the minimum number of trains he uses on his journey from home (H) to the carnival (C)?

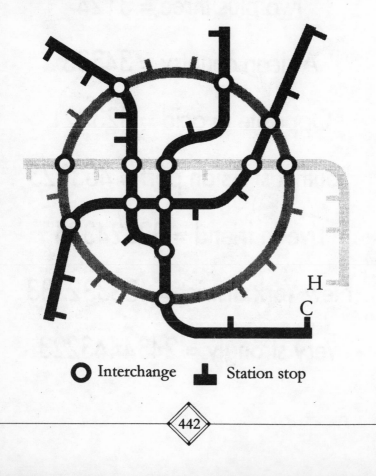

○ Interchange   ⊥ Station stop

POINT-TO-POINT

Arrange the pieces so that a trail is formed.

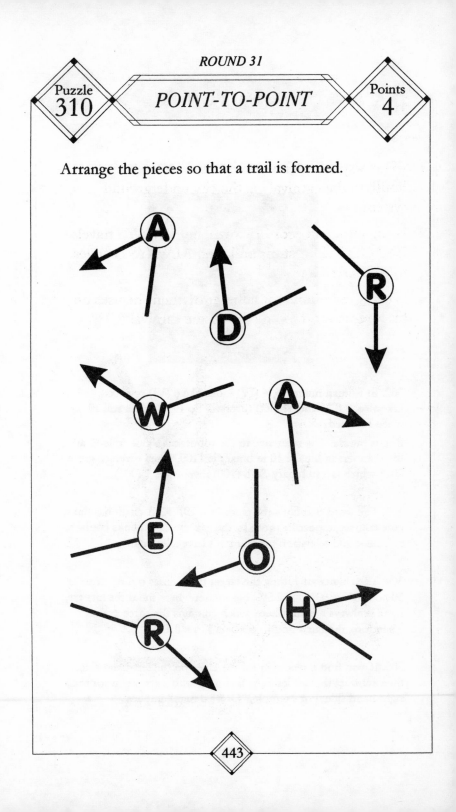

301. A Queen, King, Rook and Knight (N) are on the board as shown:

302. In Roman numerals, 4 (IV) looks like 6 (VI) reversed. Likewise, 9 (IX) and 11 (XI) reversed. So 19 (XIX) is still 19 when reversed.

Bonus puzzle: The reference to the robot was a clue to look at the numbers in binary. 10 in binary is 1100, when reversed gives 0011 which is 5 in binary. So 8 (100) reversed is 1 (001).

303. The word that links the pictures is LINK. A chain has links; golf courses, especially those by the sea, are called links courses; cufflinks; and television programmes have a linkman.

304. The chance of hitting the target three times out of three is 50% × 50% × 50% = 12.5%. No matter where the three hits are, there is always a hemisphere which contains the three points. Therefore, the fair amount to pay is $16 × 0.125 = **$2**.

305. If you find a synonym for the clues on the left-hand side, then subtract the last letter, you end up with a synonym for the right-hand side. For example, "Dress design" implies

ANSWERS

PATTERN. Subtracting the last letter gives PATTER, which is a synonym for "Chat". Continuing this for the other lines, we get ROTUND(A), CHARGE(R), BRUISE(R), SULTAN(A), DOUBLE(T), HEROIN(E) and REMAIN(S). The subtracted letters, when read from top to bottom, gives the word NARRATES which is the answer required.

306. The numbers represent the number of equilateral triangles, of any size, that can be found in the diagram. So, the final diagram should equal 6 because there are four small triangles and two larger triangles.

307. Bill's new weights are 1, 3, 9 and 27 ounces in weight. He realized that this allows him to weigh more amounts than his old set. In order to weigh an amount such as 5 ounces, he puts the 9oz weight on one pan, and the 1 and 3oz weights on the other pan, as shown below. He then adds flour to the right-hand pan until the scales balance. He has then weighed out 5oz of flour. This can be repeated for any amount between 1 and 40 ounces. Clearly, the most he can weigh out is 40 ounces, the sum of 1, 3, 9 and 27.

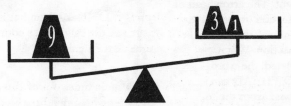

308. Each letter is encoded by the number of straight lines required to draw that letter. For example, I=1, V=2, F=3, M=4. The words in the puzzle are FIX, FIVE, KENYA, ALKALI, MANILA, FLATMATE, MANHATTAN and VEHEMENTLY.

Therefore, the top word should be encoded as 312.

309. Six different trains are necessary. This puzzle is easier if you start at C and work back to H. You find that this is pretty much the only route he could have taken, and is certainly the shortest.

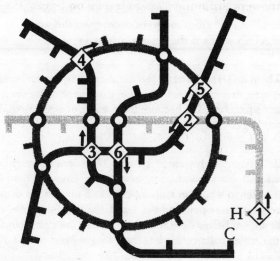

310. The answer is shown on the right. The arrowhead of each section indicates the direction of the tail of the next section. When completed, the word ARROWHEAD can be read clockwise from the top.

ROUND 32

Use this page to keep track of your score. Carry your total forward to the next round of puzzles.

Answers to Round 32 puzzles are on pages 458–60.

Category		Points	Your Score
◆	311. PIN POINTS	10	◇
123	312. ARITHMETICS	6	◇
ABC	313. FRACTION FRACTURES	6	◇
✓✗	314. SEQUENCES	10	◇
⟨?⟩	315. FORTY'S FORTE	2	◇
◆	316. BOOK ENDS	2	◇
ABC	317. ALL DIRECTIONS	4	◇
123	318. ATOMIC NUMBERS	8	◇
ABC	319. WORD FOR WORD	8	◇
◆	320. GUESSED STARS	4	◇

TOTAL FOR THIS ROUND ◇

+ Bonuses (5 points each) ◇

+ Running total from previous round ◇

TOTAL SO FAR ◆
(carry forward to next round)

If you were to pick these needles up in sequence,
which would be the middle one?

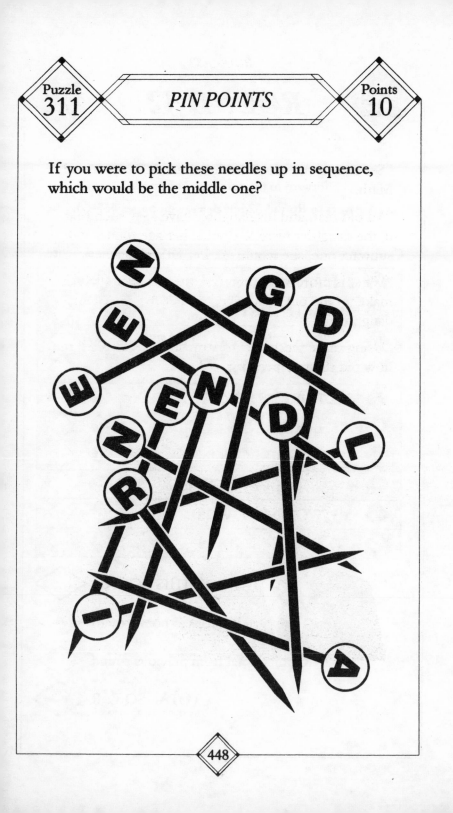

ARITHMETICS

"See if you can solve this little puzzle," says Mandy Math.

"An old man and his daughter have ages such that, if the daughter were to double her age then subtract one, she would get her father's age.

"What is more, if you reverse the two digits which make up the old man's age, you get the age of his daughter.

"Using these pieces of information, can you tell me how old the two people are?"

Wordsmith Will explains his latest puzzle. "The idea is to take the start of one word and add it to the end of a second word to make the answer.

"The fractions below give you some idea of how much of each word you need to use. I'll start you off – if you take three-quarters of 'Part of bottle' (NECK) you get NEC. Adding this to the last three-fifths of 'Church table' (ALTAR) gives NEC+TAR, the drink of the Olympian gods.

"Given that the answers on the right-hand side of the equals sign are always six letters long, can you tell me what word can be formed by taking the first letter of the six answers?"

$$\frac{3}{4} \text{Part of bottle} + \frac{3}{5} \text{Church table} = \text{Gods' drink}$$

$$\frac{2}{5} \text{Of the city} + \frac{4}{5} \text{Spy} = \text{Important}$$

$$\frac{3}{5} \text{Third month} + \frac{1}{2} \text{Card} = \text{Selling place}$$

$$\frac{2}{3} \text{Tree limb} + \frac{1}{2} \text{Human frame} = \text{Cognac}$$

$$\frac{1}{4} \text{Swop} + \frac{3}{7} \text{Warp} = \text{Obtain by compulsion}$$

$$\frac{1}{2} \text{Man's name} + \frac{2}{5} \text{Poison} = \text{By chance}$$

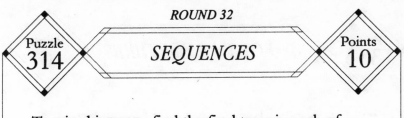

SEQUENCES

To win this game, find the final term in each of these five series.

1) O, T, T, F, F, S, S, E, N, _

2) Y, Y, H, L, Y, E, Y, T, R, R, R, _

3) R, K, B, K, Q, B, K, _

4) T, w, t, g, f, t, f, t, i, e, o, t, f, _

5) O, Y, R, T, _

"This is the simplest puzzle I could possibly give you," says Wordsmith Will in a surprisingly generous mood.

"The catch is that I'm going to give you very little to go on. Of all the usual counting numbers, one, two, three and so on, there is one number in particular that, to my mind, is rather unique.

"That number is forty. Out of the millions and trillions of possible numbers, this is the only number that possesses a certain property that I am looking for. There is nothing complicated about this property.

"Can you guess what property forty has that no other whole number possesses?"

BOOK ENDS

A hotel owner hides his spare key inside one of the telephone directories.

In case he forgets which volume contains the key, rather than leaf through every volume he has marked them in such a way that he can find out.

Can you work out which is the right directory first time?

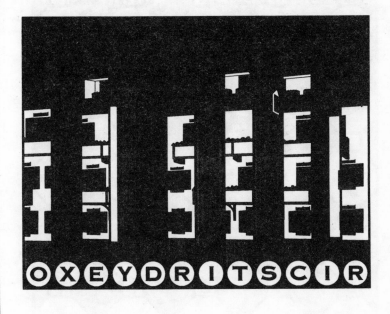

To find the correct route, first concentrate on the words in hexagons and associate them with directions.

Using the right path, something can be found.

ATOMIC NUMBERS

Professor Muddleup's Scintillating Science Sideshow is a great place to experience some fantastic fireworks, super smells and exhilarating explosions.

To create his effects, he uses elements from the Periodic Table with atomic numbers between 1 and 9 inclusive.

For his most spectacular effect, he uses four elements. If you were to multiply the atomic numbers of these four elements together, you would get the result 432.

"I'll give a special prize to anyone who can work out the atomic numbers of these elements if I tell them how heavy the lightest one is," he offers.

How can you work the answer, even without knowing the lightest element involved?

"Here's a great puzzle," says Wordsmith Will. "By now it should be obvious that I like word association puzzles, and this one's no exception.

"SEA, IRON, DOCK and EAST can all precede SIDE to make four valid phrases. Now, I want you to arrange the cards below into five rows of four so that the words in each row can all be associated with a common 4-letter word each time.

"Hey, if you're not too familiar with all the phrases, don't worry – you can always work it out using the hidden logic, as demonstrated in the example."

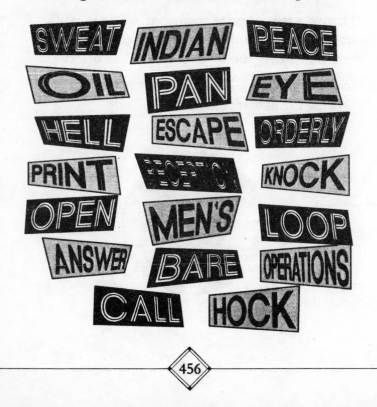

SWEAT   INDIAN   PEACE
OIL   PAN   EYE
HELL   ESCAPE   ORDERLY
PRINT   RECEPTION   KNOCK
OPEN   MEN'S   LOOP
ANSWER   BARE   OPERATIONS
CALL   HOCK

Puzzle
320

GUESSED STARS

Points
4

Sideshow Sid has a simple game. Punters are given ten star shapes and they have to arrange them to form the largest number of straight lines, with four stars in each line.

One player tried his best, but could only make three lines as shown:

How could he improve his score by two?

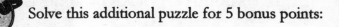 Solve this additional puzzle for 5 bonus points:

If that's too easy, is it possible to work out how to arrange ten stars into seven straight rows of four stars each? (Warning – a bit of a cheat, this one.)

311. The 'G' needle is the seventh to be picked up. In order, the needles spell out the phrase DARNING NEEDLE.

312. Express the old man's age as $10a+b$, where a is the number of tens of years he has lived and b is the number of additional single years. Using the same notation, the daughter's age is therefore $10b+a$. Doubling the daughter's age then subtracting one gives the old man's age, so:

$$2(10b + a) - 1 = 10a + b$$
$$20b + 2a - 1 = 10a + b$$
$$19b - 1 = 8a$$

The multiples of 19 that are below 100 are 19, 38, 57, 76 and 95. Of these, only the third one (57) is one larger than a multiple of 8 (namely, 56, the seventh multiple). Hence b is 3 and a is 7. Therefore the old man's age is 73 and the daughter's age is 37. This is checked by $37 \times 2 - 1 = 73$, which is correct.

313. Here are the same sums but with the answers typed in. The letters in bold make up the words on the right. The first letter of these words forms the answer NUMBER.

$$\frac{3}{4}\mathbf{NECK} + \frac{3}{5}\mathbf{AL}\mathbf{TAR} = \mathbf{N}\text{ECTAR}$$

$$\frac{2}{5}\mathbf{URB}\mathbf{AN} + \frac{4}{5}\mathbf{AGENT} = \mathbf{U}\text{RGENT}$$

$$\frac{3}{5}\mathbf{MAR}\mathbf{CH} + \frac{1}{2}\text{TIC}\mathbf{KET} = \mathbf{M}\text{ARKET}$$

$$\frac{2}{3}\mathbf{BRAN}\text{CH} + \frac{1}{2}\mathbf{BODY} = \mathbf{B}\text{RANDY}$$

$$\frac{1}{4}\mathbf{EX}\text{CHANGE} + \frac{3}{7}\text{DIS}\mathbf{TORT} = \mathbf{E}\text{XTORT}$$

$$\frac{1}{2}\mathbf{RAND}\text{OLPH} + \frac{2}{5}\text{VEN}\mathbf{OM} = \mathbf{R}\text{ANDOM}$$

314. Although these seem like ordinary sequence puzzles, they all have a hidden logic behind them. The answers are: 1) T (first letters of ONE to TEN), 2) R (final letters of JANUARY to DECEMBER), 3) R (the top line of a chess board - Rook, Knight, Bishop, King, Queen, Bishop, Knight, Rook), 4) s (first letter of each word of the question), 5) O (first letter of each of these sequences!).

315. FORTY is the only number which has its letters in alphabetical order.

316. By rearranging the directories as shown, the spines form a picture of a hotel. The key will be in the sixth directory from the left.

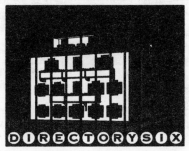

317. The correct route from the START is: UP (and over), RIGHT (on), DOWN (market), RIGHT (angled), RIGHT (of entry), UP (beat), LEFT (hand side), UP (to the elbows), RIGHT (reverend), UP (for grabs), LEFT (bank), UP (the creek), UP (your street), RIGHT (of way), DOWN (in the dumps), RIGHT (minded), UP (and coming).

Along this route, you find that you have crossed over the letters DISCOVERY, in that order.

318. The only possible combination, which has a unique smallest number, is 1, 6, 8 and 9.

319. The answer is illustrated below. Notice that taking the first letters of the the words in each row give you the answer. For example, the words Bare, Answer, Call and Knock can all precede **BACK**.

BARE	ANSWER	CALL	KNOCK	**BACK**
PEACE	INDIAN	PAN	ESCAPE	**PIPE**
	OPERATIONS		MEN'S	**ROOM**
SWEAT	HOCK	OPEN	PRINT	**SHOP**
HELL	OIL	LOOP	EYE	**HOLE**

320. Each of the ten stars can be "used" twice (calculated by 5 × 4 / 10 = 2), giving the following formation of five rows of four stars:

Bonus puzzle: You could argue that a straight line of 10 stars is in fact seven rows of four stars, the first four stars being the first row of four, starts 2 to 5 being the second row and so on.

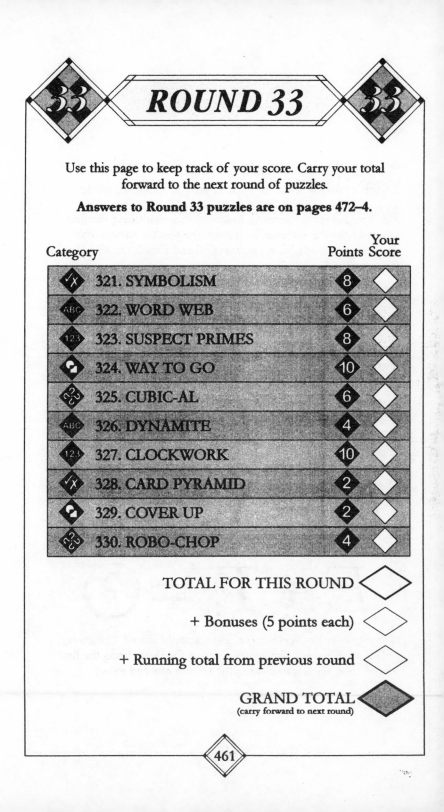

ROUND 33

Use this page to keep track of your score. Carry your total forward to the next round of puzzles.

Answers to Round 33 puzzles are on pages 472–4.

Category		Points	Your Score
	321. SYMBOLISM	8	◇
	322. WORD WEB	6	◇
	323. SUSPECT PRIMES	8	◇
	324. WAY TO GO	10	◇
	325. CUBIC-AL	6	◇
	326. DYNAMITE	4	◇
	327. CLOCKWORK	10	◇
	328. CARD PYRAMID	2	◇
	329. COVER UP	2	◇
	330. ROBO-CHOP	4	◇

TOTAL FOR THIS ROUND ◇

+ Bonuses (5 points each) ◇

+ Running total from previous round ◇

GRAND TOTAL ◆
(carry forward to next round)

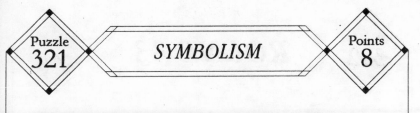
Work out what the symbols mean, then tell us
which symbol should appear in the circle in order
to make the final calculation correct.

$$O + S_1 = S_2$$

$$T_1 \times T_2 = S_1$$

$$N - S_1 = T_2$$

$$E \div T_1 = \text{\textcircled{?}}$$

WORD WEB

Which two connected words can be found in this web of letters?

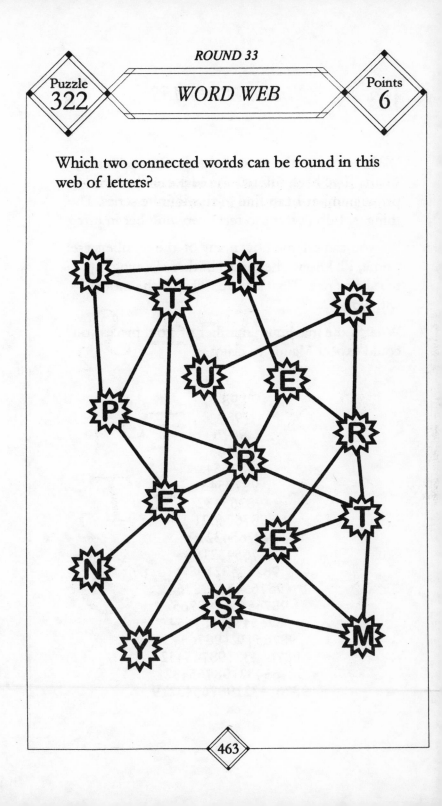

SUSPECT PRIMES

"Take a look at the series below," suggests Mandy Math. "I've been offered a gold piece for every prime number I can find in this infinite series. The thing is, I don't want to test every number in turn.

"If you can tell me how many of the numbers are prime, I'll know whether to bother claiming my reward or not. What's more, I'll split the money with you."

What is the maximum number of gold pieces you could expect Mandy to claim?

9
98
987
9876
98765
987654
9876543
98765432
987654321
9876543219
98765432198
987654321987
9876543219876
98765432198765
987654321987654
9876543219876543
98765432198765432
987654321987654321
9876543219876543219
etc.

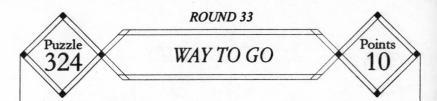

WAY TO GO

In this game, the carnival's visitors place a ball at the top of the pyramid and wait for it to drop into one of the sections at the bottom.

Where the ball has a choice, it is equally likely to choose either route.

What is the likelihood that the contestant will win a prize?

WIN   WIN

Use the arrows to slice the cube along the lines.
What number should be associated with the final
cube in order to continue the logic?

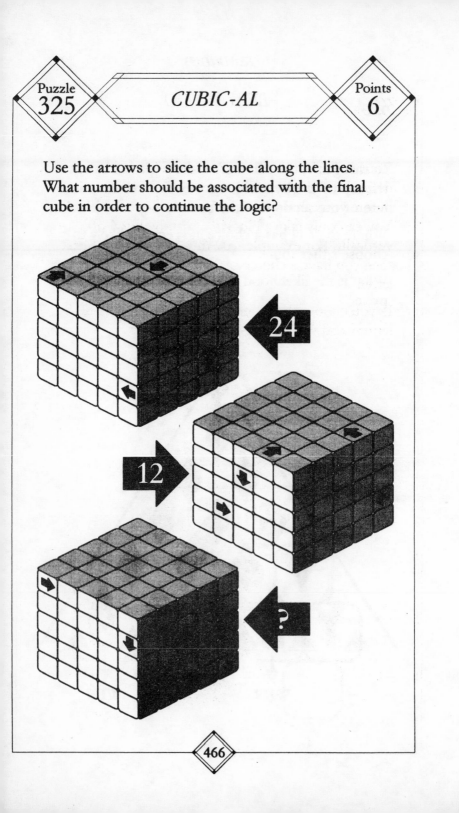

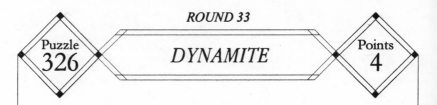

DYNAMITE

Your task, should you decide to accept it, is to defuse the bomb before it goes off. However, before you can do this you must remove the blocks. You can only take a block if it can be lifted off vertically. For example, you must take the "T" first, then you have a choice of "R" or "I" as the second letter.

If you choose the letters in the correct order, a 15-letter word will be formed.

One clockwise turn of cog A makes the minute hand of this clock turn through 360 degrees. One clockwise turn of cog E makes the hour hand turn through 30 degrees clockwise.

How many complete clockwise revolutions does cog B need to turn before "something o'clock" is again shown, and what is that time?

(To save counting, cogs A, C and E have 15 teeth; cog B has 18 teeth; cog D has 24 teeth.)

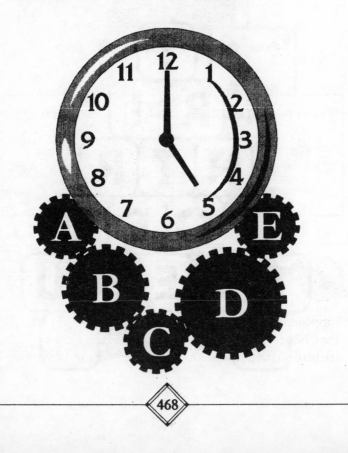

CARD PYRAMID

"Take a look at this pyramid of cards," says
Sideshow Sid. "If you can guess what card is on
top, you win the game."

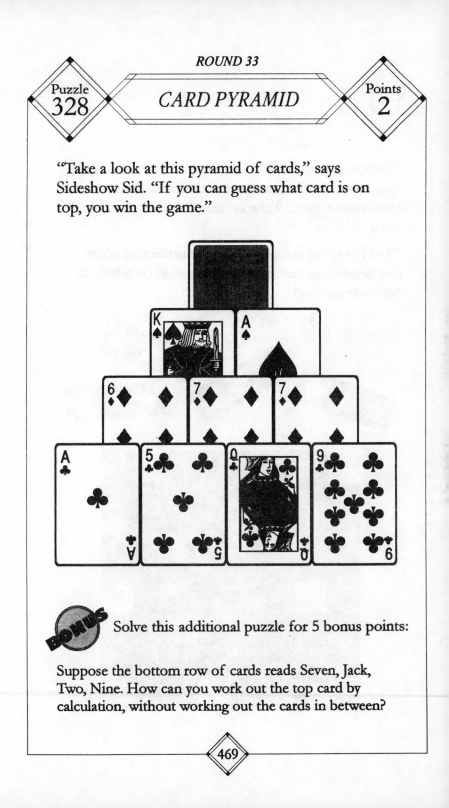

Solve this additional puzzle for 5 bonus points:

Suppose the bottom row of cards reads Seven, Jack,
Two, Nine. How can you work out the top card by
calculation, without working out the cards in between?

"Back for more, eh?" says Visual Vern. "OK then, take some of the starred triple dominoes, like the ones shown here. Take as many of them as you need.

"Tell me what is the maximum number of these dominoes you can fit onto the grid shown below. No overlapping!"

| Puzzle | | Points |
| 330 | *ROBO-CHOP* | 4 |

Fifty robots are lined up in a circle, numbered from 1 to 50.

Robot 1 is armed with a laser gun and told to exterminate the robot to his left, namely Robot 2, before passing the gun on to Robot 3. The third robot exterminates Robot 4 and passes the gun to Robot 5.

This continues around the circle until one Robot is remaining. What number robot is this?

321. The numbers 1 to 9 are coded O, T_1 (first T), T_2 (second T), F_1, F_2, S_1, S_2, E, N. Hence the sums are $1 + 6 = 7$, $2 \times 3 = 6$, $9 - 6 = 3$, and the final one should read $E / T_1 = F_1$ (that is, $8 / 4 = 2$). So F_1 is the answer.

322. NEPTUNE and MERCURY can be found.

323. Mandy will not get any gold, because none of the numbers are prime. All those ending in 5 are divisible by 5. All those ending in 2, 4, 6 or 8 will be divisible by 2. All those ending in 1, 3, 7, or 9 have a digit sum which is divisible by 3. Therefore, by a well-known mathematical rule, these numbers are divisible by 3. All the numbers have now been accounted for, so there are no prime numbers.

324. By marking the number of possible routes the ball can take at each junction and adding these numbers as we go down the pyramid, we see that there are 12 ways of reaching the left-hand WIN and 6 ways of reaching the right-hand WIN. As the total number of possible routes is $1 + 6 + 12 + 7 + 12 + 6 + 1 = 45$, and as the number of winning routes is $12 + 6 = 18$, then the probability of a win is exactly $18/45 = 0.4$. Therefore the chance of winning the game is 40%.

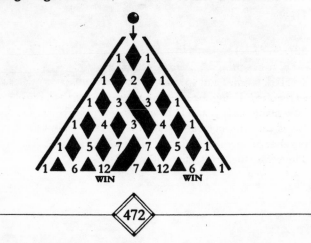

ANSWERS

325. Slice each cube along the lines pointed to by each arrow. The numbers represent the number of blocks that remain. In the final cube, the remaining blocks are in a $4 \times 2 \times 1$ formation at the front of the cube. Therefore, this should be associated with the number 8.

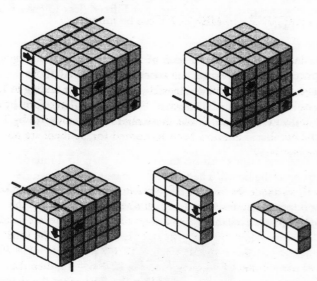

326. The word is TRINITROTOLUENE, better known as the explosive TNT.

327. Since A has 15 teeth and B has 18 teeth, then after one turn of B, A has turned 1.2 times. Therefore, if B turns 5 times, A revolves 6 times and so the minute hand points to the 12 again, as required. Using the idler principle, we need not bother with how many teeth C and D have. If B turns five turns clockwise, E will turn through six revolutions (because E has the same number of teeth as A) but in an counterclockwise direction. Therefore, the clock will show 11 o'clock.

328. The Ace of Hearts. The suits are easy – a different one is used on each row. To get the values, add together the cards to get the card above. For example, Ace plus Six gives Seven, whereas Six plus Seven gives 13. (Jack counts as 11, Queen is 12, and King is 13.) If a total goes over 13, start counting from 1 again. For example, Nine plus Six gives Fifteen (less 13 gives the answer Two).

Bonus question: Add together the values of the outside two cards and add it to triple the sum of the inner two cards. Keep subtracting 13 until you get a number between 1 and 13. In the example given (7, J, 2, 9) this would give $16 + (3 \times 13) = 55$. Subtracting four lots of 13 leaves 3. Therefore the card at the top of the pyramid in this instance would be Three of Hearts.

329. Trial and error confirms that no more than 15 dominoes can fit onto the board. The theoretical reason for this can be seen if we shade the board's diagonals as shown. Each domino must cover a light, medium and dark square, but there are only 15 light squares available.

330. Robot 37 remains.

FINAL SCORE

Well done, you've made it! Now calculate your total score. Are you a cerebral champ? Even if you aren't, a score over 800 is still very good indeed.

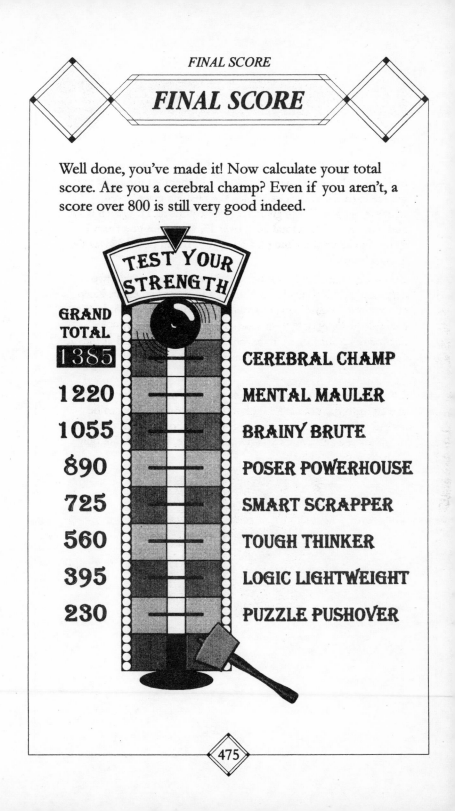

GRAND TOTAL	
1385	CEREBRAL CHAMP
1220	MENTAL MAULER
1055	BRAINY BRUTE
890	POSER POWERHOUSE
725	SMART SCRAPPER
560	TOUGH THINKER
395	LOGIC LIGHTWEIGHT
230	PUZZLE PUSHOVER

CLUES

The following pages contain some generous hints to the puzzles in the book. Don't forget there is a penalty to pay, though – you can only score half points if you read the clue.

For example, if you need the clue for Puzzle 1 before you can solve it, you score 5 points instead of the full 10.

No clues are provided for the Bonus puzzles – you are on your own for these.

PUZZLES ENDING IN –1

1. Obviously the first word is ANT. The next word starts with an E, and the 5-letter word starts with a V.

11. Nose + Piece = Nosepiece, Piece + Meal = Piecemeal...

21. This is a very old puzzle that is normally presented in a square shape.

31. You've read this word recently – for sure.

41. The O cog always looks OK. After how many "teeth moves" does the N look right (etc.)? Use the highest common factor.

51. You need to use multiplication, not addition.

61. Pirate Pete needed to make one cut in the rope before he was in the same situation as Sailor Sam.

71. Work out the factors of each number (e.g. 32 has factors of 2, 4, 8, 16) then match up with the other sides.

81. Fill in the rows with "4" and cross out the rows with "0". Now work out how it all connects up.

91. Where was the youngster playing? Hmm...

101. The shades give you a start. C goes in the top-left circle.

111. We'll start you off: B + Pointer = B + ARROW = Barrow.

121. The top-right and bottom-left corners are both the letter B.

131. The words are HORNETS, THRONES and SHORTEN. This is all the information to deduce where the letter H should be placed.

141. Three of the letter pairs can be used to prefix any of the other three letter pairs, thus giving the nine combinations required.

151. The first calculation only features the numbers 4 and 8. The second calculation is a straightforward sum.

161. This isn't hard – just use some lateral thinking. There are 56 squares, so each square must be accounted for in one of the dominoes. How is this possible? Look at the corners carefully.

CLUES

PUZZLES ENDING IN –1

171. If you draw out how the digital numbers work, you will find that nearly all of them use at least one of the right-hand segments. Concentrate on these.

181. Player 1 starts by placing the spare piece into A or B. This causes another piece to fall out of the maze, which player 2 puts back into hole G or H.

191. Start on home ground.

201. It is possible to work out how the grid divides up into groups of three squares straight away without having to consider any letters or words. LEAN appears on the top row.

211. The word I intended to type began with "W". The word I actually typed ended with "T".

221. It doesn't matter if you put the rabbits above or below the line – the puzzle is possible either way.

231. You are looking for the last letter of a word. Which word?

241. The HO/OG wheel is already in the right direction. This forms the top-left wheel of the rearrangement.

251. The word you are looking for begins with one of the "L"s.

261. Draw a line between the cat and the mouse. This should give the game away.

271. The word ARIDLY appears on the bottom right ring.

281. The number two is very important in this puzzle. There are two different sequences here.

291. TAN should be an easy spot. What other words can you see? They are all associated with the spectrum. One word uses all the letters except one. Two words are anagrams of one another, but are less well known.

301. The piece on the left-hand side is a Queen.

311. Do the letters spell anything out that might help you?

321. ONE, TWO, THREE ...

PUZZLES ENDING IN –2

2. The carnival owner thought of a way of paying less than $300.

12. 24/8 = 3 squares per section. The only possible shapes the pieces can be are: (a) a rod of 3 squares, or (b) an L-shape.

22. Black versus white squares is a useful guide. Look at the squares a knight attacks.

32. Square pens are used. The largest one encompasses all nine sheep, the smallest one pens in the middle sheep.

42. Aim for the middle-left space first.

52. Try splitting the shape into rectangles and triangles, the areas of which are easily calculated.

62. Watch out – Will meant his crossword to be viewed from outside the shop! The top row contains a place in Canada.

72. Each time, the squares that are shaded in are only connected by one side.

82. Start with R, R, D, L, D, D, R, R, U, U, U, R, R...

92. Across: incapable, happen; Down: small meal, drug.

102. The straightforward way is a zigzag. The other way crosses its own path.

112. The title of the puzzle is a big clue.

122. Andrew and Hugo aren't men.

132. Put more directly, what sort of writing would the man have to abandon because of a storm?

142. The arrow in the second column of hexagons is telling the truth.

152. First, second, fourth, eighth.

162. The bonus puzzle may be able to help you with the main puzzle. Both the black and white knights spell out an 8-letter country, and their routes are entirely separate from one another.

172. Be especially careful about card 3 – do we need to turn this over?

CLUES

PUZZLES ENDING IN –2

182. Although they are both near the Equator, they are travelling in such a way that it would be very difficult for them to meet.

192. The word can be read counterclockwise around the square.

202. Suppose there were just two houses in the street. What would the result be then? Now try it with three houses.

212. Consider what would happen if Patrick tried to do the reverse trip.

222. The separation lines will obviously possess quarter-turn symmetry. There are lots of solutions.

232. The five-letter word is MIAMI.

242. You could try taking the bags in turn and leaving any bags that would make you lose. This would give you the right answer.

252. Try approximation. This will give you an approximate result which will be more than adequate to find out what number Mandy is thinking of.

262. A lot of the words can be read both backwards and forwards, counting as two words.

272. You need to merge the squares together into groups of two and one group of three. In our solution, most of the groups are horizontal except for one group of two which is vertically aligned. Only one match around the main perimeter is removed.

282. The larger ship is made up of nine pieces, which should be familiar from the smaller ships. They should tell you the ship's name.

292. The different shades should suggest the routes required here.

302. How else can 4 and 6 be written?

312. If the man's age is 10a+b, the daughter's age is 10b+a.

322. The letters are in star shapes, which is a subtle clue to the sort of astronomical words that you are looking for.

CLUES

PUZZLES ENDING IN −3

3. There are 5 routes from A to B, so there are 5 x 5 from A to C, so there are 5 x 5 x 5...

13. Is it possible to complete the jigsaw without attaching every piece to something else?

23. Start by moving the 5 into the space, then the 4.

33. In no particular order, the words begin with B, C, E, H, T and Z.

43. The more straightforward answer contains a lot of ones. Only "2 2s" breaks this rule.

53. Eight numbers can't be made. Try adding various amounts of 4s to 0, then 7, then 14, then...

63. Why must the number 1 boat occupy the middle two squares of the first column? Now place boat 2.

73. As the pins are in a triangular formation, the shape will (to some extent) resemble a triangle.

83. Think about how many people lost in each round.

93. All the balls can take the most direct route available.

103. How can you prove it's a right-angled triangle?

113. If the first row is DCEBA, the second row is EDACB.

123. It is possible to leave one of four squares uncovered. Which ones?

133. The first letters are R, S and C.

143. How many routes are there from A to H? How many routes are there from H to C? Now you have all the information you need.

153. What do the flags for each group of countries have in common?

163. Consider green, white, red, yellow and black. This is just like a wordsearch.

173. In half a second, the left-hand wheel turns through 90 degrees. What about the right-hand wheel? A numbering system is useful to determine how the halves match up.

CLUES

PUZZLES ENDING IN –3

183. Try the same puzzle but with a square pie instead of a circular one. Once you've worked that out, use it to help solve the original puzzle.

193. The piece with the "divided by" symbol doesn't have either of its numbers utilized in the final answer. The subtraction sum results in the answer 9.

203. This is the Tower of Hanoi puzzle but with two different sorts of pieces instead of one. However, it uses a very similar principle.

213. If circles just touch at one point, that counts as one. What about if they have an overlap?

223. In either solution, you place the same number of sheep in each pen – either one or three.

233. "T" appears in the top-right corner; "E" is in the bottom-left.

243. Adding the coordinates of the squares together means that, in effect, the squares are numbered from 1 to 5 (along the top row) down to 16 to 20 (on the bottom row). Then use A=1, B=2, C=3 etc.

253. You need to use Pythagoras' Theorem three times in succession to solve this. For example, $3^2 + 4^2 = 25 = 5^2$.

263. Work out how many candy canes a teddy is worth. Likewise for the champagne. Therefore, how many tokens are needed for one sugar cane?

273. The shading of the board is very important. Which shade does each shape cover?

283. The S and the A are red herrings.

293. One word begins with T and ends with M.

303. The link is a 4-letter word.

313. 2/5 of URBAN + 4/5 of AGENT gives URGENT.

323. Clearly, no number ending in 5 will be prime. What about those ending in 2, 4, 6 or 8? What about the rest?

CLUES

PUZZLES ENDING IN –4

4. There are eight cases – consider the truthfulness of each statement for each case.

14. The cross is easy – rotate the piece by 90 degrees three times. You're on your own for the square.

24. You are looking for two pieces of personal adornment, two hues, two drinks and two musical terms.

34. A, C, E. That means the Ace must be third from the top. T, W, O means the Two is sixth from the top.

44. You can readily get to: CP??, AG??, TE?? – now consider carefully where the N must go.

54. Concentrate on the buds at the top.

64. What effect would halving the time of flight have upon the maximum height?

74. The illustration provides the clue.

84. Draw in the three diagonals on each hexagon.

94. One of the pairs makes "Finger Painting".

104. Did you never play with your calculator at school?

114. There are several ways of doing it in less than 14 moves.

124. Note you can put digits side-by-side to make new numbers, as well as the usual four mathematical operations.

134. This puzzle hinges on the interpretation of what "width" and "height" are usually regarded as. How can these definitions be used (or abused)?

144. Don't be fooled – this is less likely than you might think. How many of the possible combinations would have the cards in the ascending order?

154. In the worst possible case, how many questions would you need to ask to determine the positions of the ice cream types – two or three? Now work out how many questions you'd need to deduce the cone types.

CLUES

PUZZLES ENDING IN –4

164. Suppose you imagine the circle to be a clock face. Draw a line from 12 o'clock to 3 o'clock to 6 o'clock. What type of angle is formed? What about if the middle time is any other place along the circle? This can be used to deduce one diameter of the circle. You need two of these.

174. Why does the puzzle's title mention "cavalry"?

184. Both words begin with B.

194. What would the attacker value the most? The money or the pilot?

204. Suppose you call the first number "a" and the difference between consecutive terms "d". Then the series can be represented as 69550 = a + a+d + a+2d + ... + a+98d + a+99d.

214. There's nothing to stop you turning some of the funnels around. Have you considered what the length of each funnel is?

224. Each pair of opposing numbers has the same difference.

234. The six face will be uppermost still, but what orientation would it have?

244. Do a trial run.

254. Look for numbers and letters.

264. The darker car turns counterclockwise on the page. The first curve it comes across is the one already supplied at the bottom of the fifth column of the grid.

274. In order to win, the middle of the ball must be at least 1 foot clear from the perimeter of either of the winning hoops. Use the area of these winning regions, add them up, and divide by the area of the largest hoop.

284. Larry's preamble wasn't chit-chat – it was his way of providing a big clue.

294. Do the shapes look like the outlines of countries to you?

304. Does it matter where the three hits are on the ball?

314. The first series uses numbers, the second uses months.

324. Of the 45 possible routes, how many end up at a WIN?

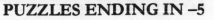
PUZZLES ENDING IN –5

5. The white ball must be in the second square on the bottom row. The yellow ball must be in the second column.

15. Place 2, 4, 6 in one shape, then place one of 2, 4 or 6 in the other three. Now continue from there.

25. 45 is no good because Mandy could advance the wheel 3, 5, 9 or 15 numbers per spin.

35. The picture is misleading. I doubt he got much sun or fresh air where he was.

45. An extra clue might be "Barney's son in the *Flintstones*" (6).

55. Watch for the con! This puzzle has a catch.

65. M = ?, but how to get the letters to fit?

75. Six shooter, Seven seas.

85. The clock has not been tampered with, but it is not in the best of working order either.

95. This puzzle requires keenness of the eye rather than keenness to do mathematics.

105. One of the shapes is a circle. The other one occurs when the ends of the rod are in opposite halves of the circles.

115. Use symmetry to your advantage.

125. Suppose all three darts hit the "1" section (total = 3). What happens to the total if one of these darts hits somewhere else?

135. The first letters of the words are (in alphabetical order) B, E, M, R and S.

145. You need to use the "opposite sides add up to 7" rule. In two of the dice, two numbers have had their positions swapped.

155. The rope was firmly tied and knotted onto the pole. How could Chaz shorten the rope using this fact?

165. Some of the small, black shapes are used in more than one of the larger shapes you are asked to draw.

175. A trial run was very helpful.

185. 1 + 1 = 2, 1 + 2 = 3, 2 + 3 = 5, etc.

CLUES

PUZZLES ENDING IN –5

195. The first section begins on the start square then goes up, up, right and on the next square up there is the first tunnel entrance.

205. The first puzzle is a murder mystery story. The second has four words, (1,1,1,8) – what do you think the first three letters would be? The film is a famous, recent thriller.

215. Ask frogs four and five to move along to pads 7 and 8 respectively.

225. It takes 15 bounces before the ball falls into one of the pockets.

235. In order to maintain the most symmetry possible, it is clear that the coin has to be placed in the middle of the mirror. Where along the middle would generate the most new lines?

245. This is a cross shape, where the white piece forms the bottom part. How do the other pieces fit together?

255. Lucy and Simon start out on red dots.

265. You may know the old puzzle about how to tell if a glass is half full. How can you use this again to tell if a glass is a quarter full? You could keep going for an eighth, sixteenth, etc.

275. Once the picture has been pieced together correctly, a message beginning "MY NAME'S..." can be read from left to right, row by row.

285. Try chopping up the middle area and see where you can fit it around the barrels. The area of the resulting shape is easy to calculate.

295. The top hat and the bow tie give the best indication. It is not D or E.

305. The last letter of each synonym needs to be changed.

315. Concentrate on the word FORTY rather than the number 40.

325. Slice the cube along the lines indicated and count how many cubes are left at the end.

CLUES

PUZZLES ENDING IN –6

6. It is an 11-letter word, appropriate to what you are seeing.

16. It's less than two! But can you see which piece to move?

26. You'll need to go backwards in order to go forwards. One of the keys is the "star" key.

36. You'd think that evens is the better bet because there are four even numbered outcomes, against odd's three. Not so.

46. The middle circle represents the letter "p".

56. If something isn't man-made, what else could it be?

66. The sum of 1 to 12 is 78, so each pair must add up to 78 / 6 = 13. The stars must add up to two pairs worth, i.e. 26.

76. Rearrange $xy=3(x+y)$ so that y is expressed in terms of x only. Then use the fact that y is a whole number.

86. What shape is always the best if you are trying to maximize areas?

96. Suppose Jamie's mother bought one of each balloon, three times over. She needs one extra of which three shapes?

106. It was a round-the-world trip. Think about circumference.

116. One of the words is PRENATAL.

126. Eliminate the squares that are protected then see which squares remain for the journey.

136. It doesn't matter which dot you start from, so choose one and consider in how many ways you can visit the remaining five dots. Don't forget that doing the route in reverse doesn't make the diagram look any different.

146. If you knew the answer to the questions, you'd know the letter you need to hit. Therefore, answer the questions for each letter in turn and decide which letter gives the unique combination of Yes and No answers.

156. Use arithmetic, shape and shade sequences to help you.

166. Assume that the guard won't recognize them, no matter where they approach him from.

488

PUZZLES ENDING IN –6

176. Don't be put off the scent – there's a way of solving this puzzle without even having to spell Pythagoras, never mind use his theorem. The clue is on the puzzle page somewhere.

186. Rotate each bangle by the same amount – there are only two possibilities you have to try, and one of them clearly won't work.

196. The paint transfers up the poles after each change of wind direction. At the end, one pole has six of its seven segments painted; the other five.

206. What might happen when the ride comes to a stop at the bottom of the U-bend?

216. Do any of the words around the square sound familiar?

226. Look at the wording of the question very carefully. The number of sides for each shape can help also.

236. Stars A and C are red herrings.

246. The middle ring has been rotated through 30 degrees; the innermost ring has been rotated a further 30 degrees.

256. There are many possible solutions which leave out the minimum number of squares. The omitted squares are isolated – there is no need to leave out a pair of squares.

266. Bear the words KENO and EMIR in mind on your travels around the cross.

276. One line from each letter is missing.

286. Mandy gave a reference to coins here. This is a rather unsubtle clue. Think about the reference to countries as well. Spot the connection?

296. Keep going along straight lines as long as possible until you can see you will be mowing some lines for a second time. In this case, turn left just before these points.

306. How many triangles can be found in the diagrams?

316. Rearrange the picture and the answer will be obvious.

326. The puzzle's title is a big clue.

PUZZLES ENDING IN –7

7. Can you see in what perspective black could lose?

17. V must be the last balloon to be popped. Use clues 1 and 4 to deduce the fourth balloon.

27. Suppose (b) is false and the rest are true then the treasure must be in B2. Suppose (c) is false... etc.

37. The word begins with C and ends with T.

47. The clue to the answer is in the first sentence.

57. All the pictures represent 5-letter words, many of which are very similar.

67. Not every puzzle piece locks with all the pieces it touches.

77. What job at the circus might crucially depend on height?

87. Although the rule is correct, so is the statement about 2000 AD. How can the two statements be reconciled?

97. No. in triangle = $|a-b| + |b-c| + |c-a|$. Notice each number is mentioned twice.

107. Which series has only one even number, at the start?

117. All you need is $5(4x+2)=20x+10=10(2x+1)$.

127. The string has two configurations at each crossover point. Thus, there are 2 x 2 x 2 = 8 possibilities. How many are knots?

137. Integer numbers mean that negative numbers are also allowed. One of these solutions contains the usual numbers 1 to 9; what numbers would work for the other solution?

147. You can't use the usual trick of turning the 6 and 9 upside-down. However, you can ...

157. It begins with P and ends with L.

167. The number you start on, two squared (4), is important. Keep adding multiples and you'll soon discover a pattern.

177. Vern's preamble was in fact a clue – if a bottle is half full, how can you verify it is also exactly half empty?

187. Trace a line out from each nail in the same fashion as a maze. Does this give you a clue of how Vern can control the game to always go his way?

CLUES

PUZZLES ENDING IN –7

197. Draw a graph with "Number of years at circus" on the y-axis and "Time" along the x-axis.

207. The "BRCHC" tile should be placed on the far left. Once you've made your selection, cause a domino effect.

217. Imagine the coins packed closely together, tilting in a different direction. Now can you see which coins to move?

227. The hour hand gives the first word of each two-word phrase.

237. The stars follow a black, white, black, white pattern throughout the maze. This should make it a lot easier to work out a suitable path.

247. If your number is 'a' and Mandy's number is 'b' then you need to use ab = a – 2b.

257. Each square can only have one of two possible letters. Make yourself a grid where you draw a pair of letters for each box. This should be a useful aid in solving the puzzle.

267. Have a careful look at the puzzle again – the diagram should tell you the necessary information.

277. The squares are not quite concentric. The smallest square has to share a match with the medium-sized square.

287. We'll start you off – BROW, CROW, CHOW...

297. The diagram in the question gives a very useful clue. Don't worry too much about the edges of the coins, it is much more useful to consider the middle points of them and where they need to fall for a win.

307. It is possible to put weights on both sides of the scales. Using this principle, how is it possible to use a 1oz and 3oz weight to weigh 2oz?

317. To start, go UP (and over), RIGHT (on), DOWN (market) and RIGHT (angled).

327. It doesn't matter how many teeth C and D have.

CLUES

PUZZLES ENDING IN –8

8. Concentrate on the number of odds and evens you have.

18. Use multiplication. Don't add anything to the first digit.

28. There are two possible answers. What is the other one? (Use trial and error, or quadratic equations if you know how.)

38. You could also add Bombay Duck to the list.

48. It's not four. It would have been if the ball was rolled along a rod of the same length.

58. Try doubling the quantity of eggs in the 6 basket as your first move.

68. The four words represented here all share a familiar property.

78. The event was less than 400 metres.

88. The first three letters of the word is something we all hate paying.

98. Make the most of what is already there. Which prisoners are already in an acceptable order?

108. Careful – the answer is not twelve. There are two positions where a square can be formed.

118. What does a circle look like if viewed at an angle?

128. There are 6 numbers but five operators, so a two-digit number must figure somewhere (in after the equals, in fact).

138. The star symbol means "go up".

148. The word that fits in the box is three letters long.

158. There is a very big clue in the puzzle title. What could the single and double rings indicate?

168. Consider the group of four pizzas on the top right. Try to cut these in half. in several different ways. Notice something in common? Now do this for the lower two pizzas.

178. The first row is HeDGe; the first column is ReCeDe.

188. The letters T, R, E go into the top circles of the diagram, in that order. The top-left circle's word reads in a different direction from the other two circles.

CLUES

PUZZLES ENDING IN –8

198. We'll start you off with (C)HASTENING, (R)EVOLUTIONARY and (A)PATHETIC.

208. It doesn't matter where you start. Suppose you place the first boulder in circle 4 and roll it to circle 1. Your next boulder should end up in circle 4.

218. BUSTLE and CACKLE are two of the words. Each coin has two possible states; how many combinations is this?

228. There is a common sense way of justifying it. Otherwise, you'll need to use the "similar triangles" mathematical rule.

238. Add up the three prices to get $4.40. What does this amount represent? It is now much more straightforward to work out the prices of each item.

248. The labels refer to the countries from which the mementoes originated. For example, the tea cup is from China. Now work out the rest.

258. It doesn't matter what angle the walls are sloping at, so long as the perpendicular height between the top of the tank and the floor remains the same as the original tank.

268. The words start with I, D and I.

278. Put another way, how is it possible for three circles to produce a total of eleven different areas? (Answer – using every overlap combination possible.)

288. Each number should be replaced by a letter throughout the story. Clearly, A=4.

298. A darlet is worth two kipples, and three skillets are worth eight kipples. Use this in conjunction with the fact about 144 ounces.

308. All the words have been encoded according to a geometrical principle.

318. 1 must be the smallest number.

328. Add up the values. If a value is greater than 13, what happens?

9. The middle square is M.

19. The first two days are: (1) A & B, C & D, E & F; (2) A & C, B & E, D & F.

29. This wordsearch is twice as easy as any other you've seen.

39. Whatever figure you're thinking of, I'd pay more.

49. There are eight possibilities. How many contain the ship?

59. This is a variant on the classic "whiskey and milk" puzzle. But does it have the same answer?

69. The binoculars is highest up and farthest right because it has the largest number of letters.

79. The black cross is easy. The white cross needs a bit of lateral thinking – how could it be formed?

89. Order the shapes in order of number of sides. Don't be fooled by the misleading word breaks.

99. The strips are already in the correct order – all you have to do is work out the start position around the cylinder.

109. What could the two staircases have in common?

119. Work out the number of handshakes for a party of 1, 2, 3, 4, 5... people then try to spot a pattern.

129. They do each other a good turn.

139. All the skewers with "4" stretch right across the grid. You can deduce that the two "1" skewers in the lower right-hand corner cross each other then stop.

149. Just because you're given something to use doesn't necessarily mean you need to use all of it to solve the problem.

159. Suppose you cut the pizza through the middle, forming exact quarters. Now imagine moving the vertical cut upwards. How does this affect the lengths of A and C?

169. B and 2 are mirror images of one another.

179. It didn't come from anywhere – Larry has had 34 birthdays, although one of them was different from the others.

CLUES

PUZZLES ENDING IN –9

189. Concentrate on all the corners first – there are a number of places where you can immediately deduce how the paths must work.

199. Put more simply, "What is the chance that the third arrow is not the best one?"

209. Ensure that the path of each new cut you make crosses the path of all earlier cuts.

219. If you wanted to lose, the worst thing you could do would be to leave a single row of chocolate, of any length. How can you avoid this position?

229. The picture is of a coffee pot. How do the curves fit together?

239. What is the speed of Mrs Jones relative to Mr Jones? Therefore, how long will it take them to meet? How far can Dilbert run in this time?

249. Try eating all of one kind, then all of the other kind. Don't forget to keep making new gums from the used ones.

259. Add this up:
$(4 \times 3 \times 2 \times 1) + 1 + (5 \times 4 \times 3 \times 2 \times 1) + (8 \times 7 \times 6 \times 5 \times 4 \times 3 \times 2 \times 1) + (5 \times 4 \times 3 \times 2 \times 1)$.

269. You need to use the intersections of the needles, so that some balls of yarn can be counted twice.

279. At the first bounce, the ball will have covered 9 feet so far. How much for the next bounce? And the next? Add these up.

289. Think carefully about the sort of numbers that MUST go along the middle line. Why wouldn't 1, 4 and 7 do?

299. The progression of moves required has a very definite pattern. Begin by twisting the tube then tilting it towards the other side.

309. Try doing the route backwards – it's quite easy.

319. The first letters of SIDE, IRON, DOCK and EAST spell ...

329. Use trial and error, or try shading the diagonals of the grid in three different tones.

PUZZLES ENDING IN –0

10. The answer is not 18 units. Think about the water levels very carefully, especially in tubes B and C.

20. The words are SUNLIGHT and HUSTLING. It is possible to deduce which letters go in the bottom and top-left circles.

30. The best clue is to consider what the numbers on the top step have in common.

40. The shaded letters posses a certain property, which the example hints towards.

50. You need to use two physical principles – light and...?

60. You might need to refer to a top row of a 5603248534 to solve this!

70. The angle at which a ball strikes a cushion is the same as the angle at which it leaves.

80. Move the pieces in the direction shown.

90. How about "Israel" for a clue? Or the author's name?

100. Use heat and light to deduce the four cases available.

110. Some of the lines only clip the edges of circles.

120. The same principle is used in a famous executive toy.

130. The synonyms are COIN, FEAR, SONG, STAR and OVAL so anagram the other two words in each line.

140. Find the solution which divides the clock into two halves. The remaining solutions all use lines parallel to this one.

150. To complete the task in such a short time, he obviously must have known a series of words which he could reel off the top of his head in a relatively short time.

160. The picture of the woman depicts her holding an umbrella. The man's picture looks as if he is checking for rain.

170. Work out what the probability is of all three numbers being different. How likely is it that your dice will be the middle of three numbers?

180. Once the clues have been entered, you can read the rows in sequence to find a 15-letter word which is sometimes happy, sometimes angry.

CLUES

PUZZLES ENDING IN –0

190. R=1.

200. Although Sid cannot use a platform more than once, there's nothing to stop him from moving where he likes on the ladders.

210. How can you arrange the pieces neatly so that you can push a piece into the middle of them, thus possibly connecting several different pieces together at a time?

220. What could be holding the egg upright? It must have been available to Marvin at the café, but small enough not to be seen.

230. Clue 2 is ASTRONAUT.

240. Make a 4 × 4 table considering the status of A and B on one side, and the status of C and D on the other.

250. It is impossible to make a triangle if any of the three lengths is over half the length of the entire chopstick.

260. None of the words in the example appear in the final solution.

270. If the consistency of the cake was all wrong, and yet Bill followed the instructions exactly, can you think of a situation in which the intended amounts are different from the actual amounts used?

280. We'll give you 1 Across : SURFACE, for one crossword, and ICE COLD for the other.

290. Try changing the numbers... but only by a little bit.

300. Say, where've I seen a puzzle like this before?

310. Although it's not necessary to realize this to solve the puzzle, a 9-letter word can be read clockwise around the route.

320. You need to count every star twice. How can this be done?

330. In the first round all the even numbered robots are exterminated. Then Robots 3, 7, 11, 15... etc. bite the dust. Keep going until one is left.

ACKNOWLEDGEMENTS

Any copyright clipart images originate from the following companies: 3G Graphics Inc., Archive Arts, BBL Typographic, Cartesia Software, Corel Corporation, Expressions Inc., Focus Designs, Image Club Graphics Inc., Imageline Inc., Management Graphics Ltd., Micrografx Inc., One Mile Up Inc., Produkturn AB, StudioAdvertising Art, Studio Piazza Xilo M.C., Techpool Studios Inc., Totem Graphics Inc., TNT Designs.

Book designed by David J. Bodycombe at Labyrinth Games using *CorelDraw!* 5, © Corel Corporation 1994.

Many thanks to:

Mark Crean, Jan Chamier, and Nick Robinson at Robinson Publishing for their efforts.

Chris Dickson, for testing the target scores.

Owen Massey, for providing a number of alternative insights into many of the puzzles.

And to my friends, wherever they are...

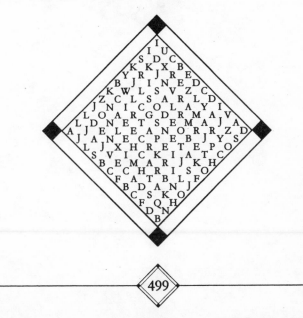